EVOLUTION &
HUMAN FOSSIL
FOOTPRINTS

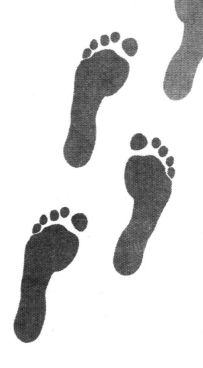

Unless otherwise specified, all Scriptures are taken from the King James Version of the Holy Bible.

Evolution and Human Fossil Footprints
© 2009, Texas Institute of Omniology

Printed in the United States of America

ISBN 1-933641-31-2

EVOLUTION & HUMAN FOSSIL FOOTPRINTS

Aaron Judkins

Table of Contents

Preface 7

Introduction 10

1. The History of Evolution 12

2. A Theory Based on Faith 14

3. The Belief Persists 22

4. A Closer Look at Darwinism 31

5. The Impact of the Darwinism 46

6. The Dilemma of Darwinism 49

7. The Fossil Record 63

8. Dating the Strata and Fossils 79

9. No Transitional Fossil Forms 95

10. Problems with the Geologic Strata 104

11. Complexity at the Beginning 112

12. No Transitional Human Forms 126

13. One Giant Leap for Mankind 132

14. The Genus Homo 150

15. The Hidden History of Homo Sapiens 163

16. Footprints: the Human Dimension 170

17. Tracking Humans 185

Conclusion 241

Bibliography 252

To the memory of Henry Johnson
—a dedicated friend who was involved
in many aspects of the Lord's service.

Acknowledgements

I would like to extend a very special thanks to Dr. Carl Baugh of the Creation Evidence Museum. It was because of his initial work that I took interest in the study of ichnology and archaeology. I have learned much about the creation model and have grown in my personal relationship with the Lord because of his life testimony. It is my honor to work with him in the Lord's service.

I also want to express my gratitude to Dr. Clifford Wilson. It is with great admiration that I have had the privilege of studying biblical archaeology under his mentorship. I have had the opportunity to put those skills to use in excavations in Israel. You are a true inspiration to the next generation.

To Tammy Juby, who spent multiple hours copyediting this work to make the information in this book understandable and readable to the non-analyst. Thanks Tammy. Thanks to Tommy Bass for reviewing the proof edition of this book. Furthermore, to all my friends and family who supported me during this work.

Lastly, to my late friend and brother in the faith, Henry Johnson, who passed away at the completion of this writing. He so eagerly helped out with comments and suggestions. This book is dedicated to you.

PREFACE

O ver the past 150 years, science has taught the theory of life origins by evolutionary concepts, finalizing theory without empirical evidence. It does not allow for questions or alternative views about our origins. It demands that life evolved with no explanation for exactly how or why. The author challenges the modern-day evolutionary interpretations of human origins by concluding that these human fossil footprints are just that—human. The evolutionary model simply is not confirmed by the empirical evidence nor is it confirmed by the fossil footprints themselves.

In most academic circles today, the interpretation of the history of Earth is defined by the narrow boundaries of the uniformitarian evolution–linear model. For example, the geology of the Earth is viewed almost exclusively in terms of uniformitarianism. This means that existing processes of erosion and volcanism are thought to be the only forces at work in the past. Because of the perceived slowness of these processes of change and the tremendous transformations observed in the Earth's depths, the age of the Earth is thus counted in billions of years; roughly 6.5 billion give or take.

Similarly, the origin of man is seen as a lengthy development from simple life form to increasingly more complex life form by evolutionary means. The simplest and supposedly earliest life form appears in Cambrian rock dated geologically at 600 million years and is thus deemed the overall age of life on Earth. Man in evolutionary form appears only in the final stage of evolution some 2.4 million years ago, the ultimate end result of evolution.

This theory has been so prevalent in modern science over the past century that all evidence, every rock, fossil, artifact, or bone, has been carefully interpreted and categorized so as to fit this model's framework to the exclusion of all others. For instance, the geologic record is counted in billions of years, the fossil record in hundreds of millions of years, and the record of humans in millions of years.

It is possible that their commitment to a particular evolutionary ideal has resulted in a process of misinterpreting the evidence. This misinterpretation by scientists has misled others to believe that these theories are backed by the evidence of evolution. However, this is not the case. Evolutionary interpretation of the evidence is weighed with a preconceived belief that humans evolved from primates. No other plausible explanations are given, nor are they encouraged. Students of archaeology, anthropology, paleontology, geology, and other sciences are taught to view any evidence with evolutionary precepts only. It is the main school of thought in scientific circles. This sorting of evidence through an evolutionary mindset has left current researchers with misinterpreted information for understanding our ideas about human origins.

In 1976, the finding of the Laetoli footprints in Africa literally put evolution back on the map. It is generally recognized that the rocks have left us a record of human activity in the past. But archaeologists have interpreted them to fit within the social paradigm of human evolution. According to evolutionary interpretation, these human fossil footprints are within the "recent" past; from the Pliocene epoch of Laetoli to the Pleistocene epoch of Australia. It is apparent that as more discoveries are made, they will continue to contradict the accepted evolutionary model. In fact, more recent conclusions by scientists show that the fossil evidence is devastating to the evolutionary model and negates the entire concept of uniformity and the evolution of man.

Yet, since Laetoli there have been other ichnological findings of human fossil footprints around the world in rock such as other volcanic ash sites and sedimentary deposit layers. These other sites are crucial to understanding the overall ichnological record. They clearly demonstrate that the anatomy of the human foot simply has not changed in form. If the evidence does not fit the macro–evolutionary theory, then an alternate suitable framework must be investigated.

Therefore, the author applies these findings to a framework of life origins that can stand up to the evidence of the fossil ichnological record. That is the creation model of the biblical record. This model (in the biblical sense) has not changed. It holds up to scrutiny, inspection, and scientific principles without compromise. Truth can change the mindsets of men and it can set them free. Simply stated, truth stands on its own. The creation model of the Bible is the framework the author applies to life origins and the evidence of the fossil record.

INTRODUCTION

One of the most exciting anthropological evidences found around the world is the phenomenon of human fossil footprints that show the consistency of the human form. The human foot shows some of the most important characteristics of human anatomy. It is what literally separates us from the so-called evolutionary ancestry tree. The anatomy of the human foot has not shown any change in the macro-evolutionary framework of origins theory. It exhibits features which are exclusively seen in the human (*H. sapiens*) footprint. These features are:

» calcaneus (heel)
» transverse arch
» lateral side of the longitudinal arch
» medial side of the longitudinal arch
» base of the fifth metatarsal
» first phalange (great toe)
» phalanges trench (digits 2 through 5), and
» areas of weight distribution

I propose that fossil human footprints are just as modern in their anatomy as modern-day footprints. There has not been any demonstrated change in the fossil record of human footprints in any strata, anywhere in the world. The defining characteristics that make human feet human are the great toe, with no opposing great toes, and the arch, which are the distinguishing traits that sets us apart from all other life forms. In fact, we are the only toed creature that lacks opposable toes.

This book contains much of the footprint material that I have shared with many people throughout the years. Since mainstream science appreciates only the evolutionary concept, I decided to dedicate the first part of this book toward dispelling this fallacy. It is most useful to understand why evolution makes the claims it does and then compare it to the evidence. The dating techniques, geologic column, and the history of mankind which evolution has taught are in complete disarray with the empirical evidence.

But before I discuss the fossil footprints, I must first dispel the evolutionary argument. It is imperative that one understands the Darwinian concept used to promote the theory of evolution and the progression from ape to man. This entails a detailed analysis of the theory of evolution, Darwinism, and the general impact this has had on academia.

CHAPTER 1

THE HISTORY OF EVOLUTION

Even though it has its roots in ancient Greece, the theory of evolution was first brought to the attention of the scientific world in the nineteenth century. The most thoroughly considered view of evolution was expressed by the French biologist Jean–Baptiste Lamarck, in his *Zoological Philosophy* (1809). Lamarck thought that all living things were endowed with a vital force that drove them to evolve toward greater complexity. He also thought that organisms could pass on to their offspring traits acquired during their lifetimes. As an example of this line of reasoning, Lamarck suggested that the long neck of the giraffe evolved when a short–necked ancestor took to browsing on the leaves of trees instead of on grass.

This evolutionary model of Lamarck's was invalidated by the discovery of the laws of genetic inheritance. In the middle of the twentieth century, the discovery of the structure of DNA revealed that the nuclei of the cells of living organisms possess very special genetic information, and that this information could not be altered by "acquired traits." In other words, during its lifetime, even though a giraffe managed to make its neck a few centimeters longer by extending its neck to upper branches, this trait would not pass to its offspring. In brief, the Lamarckian view was simply refuted by scientific findings, and went down in history as a flawed assumption.

The evolutionary theory formulated by another natural scientist that lived a couple of generations after Lamarck proved to be more influential. This natural scientist was Charles Robert Darwin, and the theory he formulated is known as "Darwinism." In his book, Darwin never mentioned the origin of life. The primitive understanding of science in his time rested on the assumption that living things had very simple structures. Since mediaeval times, spontaneous generation, the theory that non–living matter could come together to form living organisms, had been widely accepted. It was believed that insects came into existence from leftover bits of food. It was further believed that mice came into being from wheat. Interesting experiments were conducted to prove this theory. Some wheat was placed on a dirty piece of cloth, and it was believed that mice would emerge in due course. Similarly, the fact that maggots appeared in meat was believed to be evidence for spontaneous generation. However, it was realized some time later that maggots did not appear in meat spontaneously, but were carried by flies in the form of larvae, invisible to the naked eye. Even during the period when Darwin's *The Origin of Species* was written, the belief that bacteria could come into existence from inanimate matter was widespread.

Five years after the publication of Darwin's book, Louis Pasteur announced that after long studies and experiments he had disproved spontaneous generation, a cornerstone of Darwin's theory. In his triumphal lecture at the Sorbonne in 1864, Pasteur said, "Never will the doctrine of spontaneous generation recover from the mortal blow struck by this simple experiment" (Fox and Dose, 1972). Advocates of the theory of evolution refused to accept Pasteur's findings for a long time.

CHAPTER 2

A Theory Based on Faith

D arwinism is a faith that has penetrated into almost every school of thought—history, sociology, philosophy, psychology, biology, etc. I call it a faith because it is based on the belief that something is true without being a direct eyewitness to the event. Actually, most people are acquainted with this faith. You encounter it in your daily life, read its propaganda in magazines, and see its influence on television. Most of us have been taught this theory as fact from primary school on up. And the indoctrination continues via the fields of academia. It is the "faith of Darwinism."

You may think, "Darwinism is not a faith; it is a scientific theory!" and there are many people in the world who are devoted to it. Some believe that evolution is a scientifically proven fact, and the world lies under the influence of this so-called scientific position. This ideology is founded upon a series of errors and is nothing more than an illusion. The theory of evolution is a faith that denies the existence of God.

Darwinism is founded upon this denial of the Creator—the God of the Bible. It is a faith in its own right and it is one of the largest and most widespread theories in the world. It has vigorously influenced people through its various methods of misinformation and falsification, and over time generations are indoctrinated to it and the children are unknowingly taught this brand of faith.

However, creation science has dispelled evolutionary dogma by exposing gaping holes in the theory. With every new development people are once again coming face to face with the reality of creation. The faith of Darwinism is losing strength because of questions about how living things first came into existence, the flawless design and complex structure of living creatures, the variety in species, and so forth. The many recent discoveries in these branches of science show clearly and definitely that evolution is not true.

The only true fact demonstrated time and again by scientific advances is the reality of creation. If you look even with the naked eye at the living things around you, you will find the proof of an extraordinary intelligence, strategy, and design. I call it God's signature in the creation. Whether you examine a microscopic sea creature, a single atom, a cell, or the cosmos, you discover some amazing facts—the spiral design in the DNA molecule, the spiral whirling galaxies of the cosmos, the golden mean ratio, or the Fibonacci series. This superior intelligence and intricate design in every part of nature comes from the God of the Bible to whom all power and ability belong.

A person once shared with me how he became a Christian. This young man had been in trouble with the law on numerous occasions and eventually went to prison for his crimes. He told me that while he was in prison he began to research the world's religions in order to learn which offered the truth. After years of research on numerous religions, he came to a realization. There was only one religion which offered scientific backing and empirical evidence for the origins of life. His conclusion: the Bible was the only book that was backed by the evidence. Nevertheless, the Darwinian theory still continues to thrive as an accepted belief system.[1]

Since the Darwinian theory first appeared, a large number of scientific findings have invalidated its claims one by one. The development of the electron microscope, new knowledge of genetic laws, the discovery of the structure of DNA, the revelation of the complexity of every living organism, and other modern advances have defeated Darwinism and will continue to oppose it.

But despite the fact that science is developing quickly and is con-

---

1. Grene, M. (1959, November). *Encounter,* p. 48.

tinually introducing something new into our lives, certain scientists continue to defend theories developed in the nineteenth century, theories that were developed with a primitive scientific understanding whose naiveté and superficiality would make a child laugh.

So why is Darwinism still so popular in some scientific circles when there is not even one concrete scientific proof in place? On the contrary, it is clearly evident that every living thing has been created according to a flawless design and that nothing has come into existence by chance, as the theory of evolution claims. How can it then be that many people continue to be strong advocates of this theory?

The reason is this: the theory is more an expression of a mentality and belief than a scientific formulation. It is a mentality that does not view evolution as a mere theory whose validity can be investigated by scientific method, but as a belief that must be vindicated at all costs. Because their faith cannot be substantiated by scientific facts, people with this mentality have a fixed bond with their theory which cannot be influenced by the scientific proofs that refute it. No matter how convincing the evidence against evolution, evolutionists continue to ignore it and vigorously defend their faith.

For Darwinists, the theory of evolution is much more than a scientific proposition. When their theory becomes a matter for discussion, evolutionist scientists immediately lose their impartiality and scientific objectivity. They are so fiercely bound to their theory that most distinguished biologists "would rather lose their right hands than begin a sentence with the phrase, 'If the theory of evolution is true.'..."[2] They do not even want to consider that the theory of evolution might be wrong.

People are not accustomed to seeing this attitude among scientists. They generally imagine that scientific discourse is independent of the individual scientist's philosophical and ideological prejudices and that the scientists are objective individuals whose facts are substantiated by concrete evidence and whose truths are proven by experiments. For this reason, they seldom doubt the correctness of

2. "Darwin's Death in South Kensington," *Nature,* February 26, 1981, vol. 289, p. 735

the theory of evolution. This is a great error, however, because when evolutionist scientists are discussing the theory of evolution, scientific criteria are not brought to bear on the issue. These words of the eminent Darwinian, Pierre Teilhard de Chardin, expose the position of "science" in the Darwinist outlook: "Is evolution a theory, a system, or a hypothesis? It is much more. It is a general assumption to which all theories, hypotheses, and systems must acknowledge and which they must satisfy in order to be true. Evolution is an ideal which postulates all facts, a course which all schools of thought must follow. This is what evolution is" (Ayala, 1977).

As can be seen in this quotation, the terms used by Darwinists when they speak of their theory give important clues about their dogmatic attitude and blind allegiance. Taking other examples, one of the leading evolutionists of the world, G. W. Harper, calls the theory of evolution a "metaphysical belief" (Harper, 1979, p. 16). The Harvard evolutionary biologist Ernst Mayr calls it "man's world view today" (Mayr, 1978, p. 47). Sir Julian Huxley, probably the most prominent evolutionist of the twentieth century, saw evolution as "a universal and all–pervading process" and, in fact, nothing less than "the whole of reality" (Huxley, 1955, p. 272). Following these definitions, H. S. Lipson has reached the following conclusion: "In fact, evolution became in a sense a scientific religion; almost all scientists have accepted it and many are prepared to 'bend' their observations to fit in with it" (Morris, 1989).

When evolutionary literature is examined, one will encounter many examples of the religious nature of this belief and see that it looks at every social and psychological phenomenon from the point of view of the theory of evolution. L. C. Birch, a biologist from the University of Sydney and P. R. Ehrlich, a biologist from Stanford University, describe the evolutionary doctrine this way: "Our theory of evolution has become . . . one which cannot be refuted by any possible observation. Every conceivable observation can be fitted into it. It is thus 'outside of empirical science' but not necessarily false. No one can think of ways in which to test it. Ideas either without basis or based on a few laboratory experiments carried out in extremely simplified systems have attained currency far beyond their validity.

They have become part of an evolutionary dogma accepted by most of us as part of our training."[3]

This inflexible position of modern evolutionists is even more rigid than that of Darwin himself. When Darwin proposed this theory, he left room for the possibility that he could have made a mistake. In his book *The Origin of Species,* he often began his expositions with the words, "If my theory be true. . . ." In his investigations it can be seen that Darwin accepted certain scientific criteria and proposed some ways his theory could be examined. For example, he wrote about the fossil record: "If my theory be true, numberless intermediate varieties, linking most closely all of the species of the same group together must assuredly have existed. . . . Consequently, evidence of their former existence could be found only amongst fossil remains" ("Darwin," 1964, p. 179).

The numberless intermediate varieties mentioned by Darwin have never been found, and today many evolutionist paleontologists have had to concede this. When taking into account Darwin's condition for "if my theory be true," his theory must be rejected. If he were alive today, perhaps Darwin would have abandoned his theory for this very reason.

THE FUNDAMENTALS OF DARWINISM

Although it is expected to credit the beginning of this theory to Charles Darwin, an elementary form of this can be traced back to the beginnings of written history. In fact, the belief that life had its origins in a single basic substance is so widespread among the peoples of the world, primitive or civilized, that it can be considered one of the few universal themes in the history of ideas (Able, 1973).

Darwinism rejects the truth of the Bible. The study of world religions shows that a large number have been influenced by one another, and many similarities can be detected between their beliefs and doctrines from ancient cultures. The ancient religions of Greece and Mesopotamia form the basis of Darwinism. Contrary to what a large

---

3. L. Birch and P. Ehrlich, "Evolutionary History and Population Biology," *Nature,* 216 (1967), pp. 352, 369.

number of people believe, Darwinism is not an established scientific theory based on facts, observation, and experiment, but merely a rationalistic attempt to explain the universe.

Darwinism did not begin with theories established by observations and empirical evidence collected by scientists in the nineteenth century. Its origins go back to much earlier secular philosophies. Darwinist beliefs were first encountered a few thousand years ago in the polytheistic and secular religions of Greece and Sumeria. Therefore, Charles Darwin was not the first person to put forward the idea of evolution; he was an amateur researcher who traced the main outlines of a basic belief, gave form to its doctrines, and later established a theory.

A Sumerian tablet describing the stages, according to their superstitious belief, in the creation of human beings upon the order of the water god.

The inscriptions of Sumeria, which deny God and assert that living things came to be through an evolutionary process, form the backbone of the religion of Darwinism.[4]

When Sumerian inscriptions were examined, they revealed a legend stating that first there was a watery chaos and out of that two gods emerged: Lahmu and Lahamu. According to this belief, the two gods first created themselves and later, as they evolved, brought other material and living things into existence. In other words, life appeared all at once from the lifeless, watery chaos. The evolutionists' belief that living things first formed from lifeless matter has much in common with the Sumerian belief that the universe developed through an evolutionary process.

When ancient Egyptian religion is examined, the same beliefs are found; snakes, frogs, worms, and mice were said to be created from the mud deposited by the flooding of the Nile. In other words, the Egyptians believed that living things came out of the mud at random. The myths of both the Egyptians and Babylonians include the

---

4. K. Cumming (April 4, 1998), "The Collapse of the Theory of Evolution; the Fact of Creation," *Conference Speech.*

concept of a primordial sea from which the Earth and life arose. And history reveals that they worshipped many of them as gods.

It is erroneous to think that this concept has now disappeared into the mists of history and perished along with ancient civilizations. Today, evolutionists maintain the same idea. They would have the scientific world believe that first there was the sea, the watery chaos, or, as they call it, "primeval soup." According to the theory of evolution, inanimate chemical elements necessary for the development of life (such as carbon and phosphorus) came together in water under the right conditions and in the right proportions by chance four billion years ago. In the meantime, there were lightning storms and quakes, and the first building blocks of life, amino acids, came into being. By the same operation these amino acids became proteins, proteins formed cells, and, through the continuation of this chain of random occurrences, human beings finally came to be. However, the claim that lifeless matter can coalesce and form life has not been verified in any observation or experiment; it is an extra–scientific claim. Every living cell comes into existence from the division of another living cell, the process of cellular mitosis. No one in the world, even in the most advanced laboratory, has succeeded in making a living cell from non–living material, which shows that the first cell was most certainly created with conscious intent.

One of the greatest obstacles in Darwinism is the question of how living things first came into being. Evolutionists generally prefer to avoid this question because the most concrete answer they can give is no different from that given by religions of centuries ago. During the period in which Darwinism developed, false beliefs about the formation of living things were prevalent; flies came from sweat, frogs from mud, and ants from sugar.

One of these nonsensical beliefs is that of punctuated equilibrium. Since the hoped for transitional fossil forms had not been found, some evolutionists were under a good deal of pressure. So they decided that there was no need for transitional forms because the transition from one species to another had happened suddenly. However, it is no different from the claim that ants came from sugar. The first bird emerged suddenly from a reptile egg and later, in the same way, another bird came by chance from another egg. These two birds came together, and a bird family formed. A similar theory proposed by Charles Darwin is that bears who spent a lot of time in the water changed into whales over time. However, today's scientific facts clearly demonstrate how deceptive this claim is.

Chapter 3

The Belief Persists

O ne of the prominent characteristics of ancient religions is the attribution of power to statues and other objects of wood or stone, which cannot speak nor have any life. Interestingly, similar beliefs can be seen among modern evolutionists. As the ancients believed that lifeless statues had power to create, evolutionists believe that lifeless matter composed of unconscious atoms has creative power. They claim that lifeless materials came together by coincidence, organized themselves, and formed living beings with flawless, highly complex characteristics. In Israel's ancient history, the nation went into idolatry and, in Jeremiah's time, worshipped the "queen of heaven," making cakes and drink offerings to her despite God's commandment to have no other gods before Him. Most prominent among idols is one that has changed only in name since ancient times—"nature." The Gnostics continue this type of worship and today know her as "Mother Nature."

Tornadoes, earthquakes, and floods are attributed to "the anger of Mother Nature" or are seen as "expressions of nature," but no one has any actual explanation for this power that is called "nature." This same belief was present in societies of the past, but under a different name. In Greek mythology Mother Nature was called "Gaia," and in ancient religions was known as the goddess of plenty. What evolutionists have done is simply to change the names and symbols, attributing the same power to unconscious atoms. To believe in the creative power of coincidence, inanimate matter, or unconscious atoms is certainly a travesty of reason. Just as the ancients believed that lifeless idols created things, so evolutionists believe that lifeless material formed into living things. The origin of this belief is the view that everything is somehow divine, that inanimate matter is possessed of intelligence and will, and that it is capable of making decisions and implementing them.

SUN WORSHIP

Another similarity between evolution and those of ancient societies is that both are based on sun worship. Sun worship goes back to the earliest periods of history. People knew the sun provided them with light and heat, so they felt indebted to this celestial body and considered it a god. In the past this belief kept many people suppressed from the truth about the Creator, the God of the Bible.

It is true that the sun provides the world with light and heat, but the one who deserves credit for this is God, the one who in the book of Genesis created the sun. The sun is a material mass without consciousness. There was a time when it did not exist, and there will be a time when its fuel will be exhausted and it will be extinguished. He created the sun from nothing, like all heavenly bodies, and therefore it is Him who should be praised and glorified for its existence.

It is interesting that modern evolutionists repeat the basic beliefs of historical sun worshippers by proclaiming that they owe their existence to a "big bang" or some sort of energy. When the beginnings of evolution are considered, the sun is acknowledged as the source of every living thing in the world. According to ancient cultures, light from the sun caused the appearance of the first living things on the Earth. Later, it was the sun's energy that caused the formation and mutation of living species. The approach of evolutionists in this regard was best summed up by the evolutionist Carl Sagan. In his book *Cosmos,* Sagan said, "If we must worship a power greater than ourselves, does it not make sense to revere the sun and stars?" In the same book, he wrote, "Our ancestors worshipped the sun, and they were far from foolish" (Sagan, 1980, p. 243).

Carl Sagan's teacher, the evolutionist astronomer Harlow Shapley, is known for saying, "Some piously record, 'In the beginning,

God . . .' but I say, 'In the beginning, hydrogen.'" Shapley believed that the first element that existed was hydrogen and that this gas, in the course of time, developed by itself into human beings, animals, and trees. At the root of these ideas is the idea of "Mother Nature." But anyone using their intelligence can understand that the universe is not a product of lifeless and unconscious matter; on the contrary, they will see in every detail extraordinary design and intent. But to-day some people are stubbornly persistent in their belief in evolution and willingly deny the existence of the Creator of the universe. The fallacy continues, "In the beginning hydrogen. . . ."

THE DISSENT FROM GOD

The reality that the evolutionist mind can never accept is that God exists and that He created the universe perfectly and with a purpose. However, it only takes a moment's thought to understand this obvious reality. Exodus 20:11 says: "For in six days the LORD made heaven and earth, the sea, and all that in them is, and rested the seventh day: wherefore the LORD blessed the sabbath day, and hallowed it."

Today, no scientist with an objective mind can defend the above list of beliefs because science has demonstrated that living things were created according to a magnificent design with intelligence and plan. One of the most prominent names in the increasingly widespread "intelligent design" theory is the American biochemist Michael J. Behe, who writes: "The dilemma is that while one side of the [issue] is labeled intelligent design, the other side must be labeled God" (Behe, 1996, p. 232).

Evolutionists will be held accountable by God's Word in Romans 1:20: "For the invisible things of him from the creation of the world are clearly seen, being understood by the things that are made, even his eternal power and Godhead; so that they are without excuse."

GREEK PHILOSOPHY

The precursor of Darwinist ideas was presented by Greek Milesian philosophers who had no knowledge of the laws of physics, chemistry, or biology. One of the most important assertions of these philosophers that included Thales, Anaximander, and Empedocles, was that living things (animals, human beings, and plants) were generated spontaneously from inanimate elements such as air, fire, and water. According to this theory, the first living things came into being suddenly and spontaneously in water, and after a while some creatures left the water and adapted to living on land.

The first of these Milesian philosophers was Thales. He lived in a coastal city and spent a long time in Egypt, where he was influenced by the importance of the Nile River in the lives of its inhabitants. He became obsessed with the idea that living things could generate themselves from water, a conclusion he had reached by the use of simple logic and inference, but with no experiment or scientific observation. Later, other Milesian philosophers established theories on the basis of that same logic.

After Thales, the most important thinker was his pupil Anaximander, who contributed two important doctrines to the annals of human thought. The first of these was that the universe has always existed and will continue to exist into eternity. The second was an idea that had begun to take shape in the time of Thales: that living things evolved from one another. Anaximander even wrote a poem called "On Nature," which is the first literary work to contain a theory of evolution. In this poem he wrote that creatures arose from slime that had been dried by the sun. He assumed that the first animals were covered with prickly scales and lived in the seas. As these fish–like creatures evolved, they moved onto land, shed their scaly coverings, and eventually became human beings. Philosophy books explain how Anaximander shaped the foundation of the theory of evolution:

"We find that Anaximander of Miletus (611–546 B.C.) advanced the traditional evolutionary idea, already quite common in his day, that life first evolved from a type of prebiotic soup, helped along a bit by the rays of the sun. He believed that the first animals developed from sea slime which had been evaporated by the sun rays. He also believed that men were descended from fish."[5]

---

5. www.thedarwinpapers.com

We find a similar explanation in Charles Darwin's book *The Origin of Species*. There is basically no difference between the theory of evolution proposed there (in spite of its pseudoscientific claims) and the account of the Milesian philosophers who lived in the culture of ancient Greece.

The most important element of Darwin's theory, the concept of "natural selection," also has ancient Greek roots. The thesis that natural selection is due to a struggle for survival among the species is first encountered in the work of the Greek philosopher Heraclitus. According to Heraclitus' thesis, there is a constant struggle among living things. In a sense, this is the origin of Darwin's theory of natural selection 2,500 years later.

Empedocles (495–435 B.C.), who lived later than Thales and Anaximander, believed that everything present on the Earth came to be through random intermixtures of varying proportions of water, air, fire, and earth. The writer David Skjaerlund, who has investigated the philosophical roots of the theory of evolution in his book *Philosophical Origins of Evolution,* states that Empedocles had some interesting ideas. He "believed that chance alone was responsible for the entire process and that man had developed from prior plant life."[6] The concept of chance in ancient religions is a basic belief and is also the most important aspect of the faith of Darwinism.

Democritus is another Greek philosopher who contributed to the theory of evolution and to those secular philosophies that take the theory for their foundation. According to Democritus, the universe is composed of small particles called atoms and, apart from matter, nothing exists. Atoms have always existed—uncreated and indestructible. Hence, matter has always existed and will continue to exist into eternity. Democritus rejected any kind of spiritual faith and claimed that spiritual values, even morality, can be reduced to atoms. Thus, Democritus has been called the first true secular philosopher; to him the universe has no purpose, everything moves according to a blind necessity, and everything came into being spontaneously by itself.

---

6. www.forerunner.com

Unconscious atoms composing the universe—the world, the air we breathe, what we eat and drink, our bodies—in short, everything we perceive, are central to the Darwinian theory. It is well known that every living thing is made up of atoms of carbon, hydrogen, and other elements. Darwinism claims that these atoms came together by random chance. According to this claim, various atoms were formed by some unknown impulse and later came together to form stars, planets, and all heavenly bodies. After a time, atoms again came together by chance to form a living cell with a highly complex structure. Then this living cell underwent a process of evolution to form living things with extraordinarily elaborate systems, and finally, human beings with a highly developed consciousness. Moreover, the human being who is totally the result of chance, with the aid of instruments developed by chance (such as the electron microscope), has discovered the atoms from which he is formed!

Thus, the theory of evolution accepts as fact that every atom has creative intent and power to bring about life. Evolutionists claim that these lifeless atoms came together, created a human being, and that later this amalgamation of atoms decided to go to college and have a career. However, every experiment and observation has shown that without conscious organization, matter is never able to organize itself; on the contrary, it advances toward disorder and chaos. This is known as the Second Law of Thermodynamics, or the Law of Entropy. For this reason it is obvious that nothing in the universe results from chance but has been brought into existence by an intelligent being. I propose this intelligence to be just who He said He was in the Bible: the Alpha and the Omega; the Eternal God; I AM of Genesis, who created both Heaven and Earth.

Another important contributor to the faith of Darwinism was the Greek philosopher Aristotle. According to Aristotle, species can be arranged in a hierarchy from the simplest to the most complex and aligned in a linear form like steps in a ladder; he called this thesis the *Scala Naturae*. This idea of Aristotle's would deeply influence western thought until the eighteenth century and was later to become the origin of belief in the Great Chain of Being, which in turn, became the theory of evolution.

THE GREAT CHAIN OF BEING

The underlying idea of Darwinism—that every living thing evolved from matter—is first encountered in the concept of the Great Chain of Being by the Greek philosopher Aristotle. This is an evolutionary belief still popular with those philosophers who deny the existence of God. The Greek idea that the first living thing spontaneously produced itself from water became the doctrine of the Great Chain of Being. According to the *Scala Naturae* which had been accepted for 2,000 years, living things formed by themselves, evolving from minerals to organic matter, to living organisms, to plants, to animals, to human beings and, finally, to "gods."

According to this belief, new organs formed by themselves conforming to the needs of nature. Originally, the idea was proposed only as a philosophical view. According to this specious reasoning, small living things became larger living things stage by stage; every living thing has its place in the chain. It also asserts that stone, metal, water, and air became living organisms which became animals, and animals became human beings without any interruption in the process. The reason this belief (which has no scientific foundation, contradicts all scientific facts, and stands only on abstract logic) has won acceptance for so long is not a scientific one but an ideological one. What allows this belief to endure is a strict approach that denies the existence of the Creator. This belief over the eons of time has periodically changed its name and has been elaborated upon. Today, we know it as the "theory of evolution."

Aristotle rejected the existence of a Creator who created all things from nothing and instead presented the view of gods having evolved from human beings. With this unsound deduction, Aristotle greatly influenced Greek philosophers. The period in which the *Scala Naturae* came into western thought coincides with the advent of humanism and the Renaissance. At the beginning of the fifteenth century Greek and Latin works were brought into Europe and entered the current of western thought and philosophy. Foremost in these texts was the denial of the existence of a supernatural Creator.

In atheistic thought, human beings have full capacity to control themselves and the world they live in, and it denies that there is life after death. The Great Chain of Being formed the basis of this belief by stating that human beings came into being by chance, the result of an evolutionary process, and were essentially nothing more than lumps of matter. Thus, moral values and human feelings have no importance; a person should simply enjoy each day he lives and feel responsible to no one. In time, Aristotle's concept of divinity at the top of the *Scala Naturae* was replaced by the humanist idea of man as the highest being.

The Great Chain of Being was quite popular from the Renaissance until the eighteenth century and exerted much influence on the scientists of that era. French scientists Benoit de Maillet, Pierre de Maupertuis, Comte de Buffon, and Jean Baptiste Lamarck, among others, were men who had appropriated the Greek notion of the Great Chain of Being and who had a strong influence on Charles Darwin. They based their scientific research on this evolutionist view. The common tenet of these men was that the various living species were not created individually. Instead, they came into existence spontaneously through a process of evolution dependent on natural conditions, a model similar to Darwin's. For this reason it can be said that modern evolutionary thought was born in France.

The French evolutionist Comte de Buffon was one of the most well-known scientists of the eighteenth century. For more than 50 years he was the director of the Royal Botanical Gardens in Paris. Darwin based much of his theory on Buffon's works. In his 44-volume work *Histoire Naturelle,* it is possible to find most of the elements that Darwin used.

The Great Chain of Being was the base of the evolutionist systems of both de Buffon and Lamarck. The American historian of science, D. R. Oldroyd, defines their relationship in these words:

> In his *Histoire Naturelle,* Buffon reveals himself as an exponent of the doctrine of the Great Chain of Being, with man being placed at the top of the Chain. . . . Lamarck held a version of the ancient doctrine of the Great Chain of Being. Yet . . . it was not conceived as a rigid, static structure. By their struggle to meet the requirements of the environment, and with the help of the principle of the in-

heritance of acquired characteristics, organisms could supposedly work their way up the Chain—from microbe to man, so to speak. . . . Moreover, new creatures were constantly appearing at the bottom of the Chain, arising from inorganic matter through spontaneous generation. . . . Ascent of the Chain involved a continuous process of complexification, due to the so–called "power of life."

—Oldroyd, 1983, pp. 23, 32

As one can clearly see, what is called the "theory of evolution" is really a transfer to modern times the ancient Greek myth of the Great Chain of Being. There were evolutionists before Darwin, and most of their ideas and so–called proofs were already found in the concept of the Great Chain of Being. With de Buffon and Lamarck, the Great Chain was offered to the scientific world in a new form which influenced Darwin.

Indeed, Darwin was so influenced by this idea that he based his whole theory on its basic logic. In the book *Darwin's Century,* Loren Eiseley points out that Darwin made use of the eighteenth century concept of the scale of existence in *The Origin of Species* and that the idea that whole organic matter tended inevitably to "progress toward perfection" found its origin there (Eiseley, 1961).

Therefore, Darwin did not propose a new theory. What he did was nothing more than to give it new expression in contemporary scientific language. Based on a few deceptive observations, a religion going back to the myths of the Sumerians and ancient Greeks was sustained. It was enhanced in the seventeenth and eighteenth centuries with new additions by many scientists. Later, through Darwin's *The Origin of Species,* the theory gained a scientific veneer and became the greatest falsehood in the history of science.

CHAPTER 4

A Closer Look at Darwinism

. . . Thinking of so many cases of men pursuing an illusion for years, often a cold shudder has run through me, and I have asked myself whether I may not have devoted my life to a fantasy.

—Charles Darwin[7]

In order to understand Darwinism, it is first necessary to abandon some preconceived ideas. What one has read so far does not demonstrate the real attributes and goals of this religion but only the ideas that bring people under its influence. Darwinism has been represented by evolutionists as a scientifically proven truth revealed by Charles Darwin; however, science has more recently invalidated the claims of Darwinism one by one. Because there is no longer a scientific foundation for the theory of evolution, it now relies only on methods of misinformation through which evolutionist thought is still being imposed on contemporary people as a scientific fact. To

---

7. Charles Darwin's letter to C. Lyell, November 23, 1859, cited in Francis Darwin, *The Life and Letters of Charles Darwin,* vol. II, New York; D. Appleton and Company, 1888, p. 25.

understand every aspect of Darwinism it is first necessary to escape the influence of evolution and uncover the truth.

CHARLES DARWIN

When evolution is mentioned today, the first name that comes to mind is Charles Darwin. Regardless of the fact that belief in evolution lies at the root of many ancient religions, the one who brought the concept into its present form was Darwin. To get to know the religion of Darwinism, one must first overcome an important myth which has grown up about Darwin over the past 150 years. Charles Darwin has been presented as a brilliant, successful man of science, an objective researcher. The fact that he is remembered in evolutionist circles as "the greatest scientist" and the "genius of the century" is basically due to misinformation. When Darwin's life and ideas are scrutinized, it becomes clear that this is not the case.

Darwin, contrary to what everyone thinks, was neither an important scientist, nor the "lord of the species" who solved the mysteries of nature. The founder was a layman who received a Protestant education and did not complete his medical studies. Darwin was an amateur researcher who was afflicted by many undiagnosed illnesses. He was distant and avoided arguments. His mind was full of doubts, he had difficulty in thinking logically, he was solitary, and he lived in a confused, spiritual mindset. In an emotional reaction to the death of his young daughter, he became rebellious against God and religion. It was in this unhealthy spiritual state that he proposed his thesis that would later become known as the "foundation of atheism."

Darwin first preached the detailed fundamentals of the theory to important scientists in his circle through conversations, articles, and personal letters. What Darwin left unfinished or insufficiently elaborated was completed by his followers, who subsequently continued to expound the theory.

Darwin's *The Origin of Species,* which is revered as if it were a holy book, is actually full of impasses and contradictions and is based on an inconsistent logic relying on mere probabilities and guesses. Darwin himself regarded his book not so much as a scientific work but as "a long argument." Darwin acknowledged the weaknesses, inconsistencies, and difficulties of his theory in his writings and in letters to friends. In one letter he confessed that there were serious flaws in the theory which had brought him to the point of suicide: "You ask about my book, and all that I can say is that I am ready to commit suicide; I thought it was decently written but find so much wants rewriting. . . ."[8] In another letter, he said: "Pray do not think that I am so blind as not to see that there are numerous immense difficulties in my notions."[9]

Particularly in letters to his friend Charles Lyell, he clearly expresses the doubts he felt in regard to his theory: "Thinking of so many cases of men pursuing an illusion for years, often a cold shudder has run through me, and I have asked myself whether I may not have devoted my life to a fantasy."[10]

Moreover, Darwin was aware of errors and unfounded claims in his theory. He wrote: "Long before having arrived at this part of my work, a crowd of difficulties will have occurred to the reader. Some of them are so grave that to this day I can never reflect on them without being staggered" (Darwin, 1882, p. 204).

In a letter to his close friend Asa Gray, he defined his theory as extra-scientific speculation: "I am quite conscious that my speculations run quite beyond the bounds of true science" (Gillespie, 1979, p. 2).

Some later scientists have also pointed to Darwin's contradictory spirit and unsound logic. The fact that the founder of a theory which was presented to the world as absolute reality had a mind filled with contradictions and doubts gives rise to serious misgivings about the foundation upon which the theory was built. The American physicist Lipson has this to say about Darwin's fears: "On reading *The Origin of Species,* I found that Darwin was much less sure of himself than he is often represented to be; the chapter entitled 'Difficulties of the Theory,' for example, shows considerable self-doubt.

---

8. Ibid, vol. II, p. 501.
9. Ibid, vol. I, p. 395.
10. Ibid, vol. II, p. 25.

As a physicist, I was particularly intrigued by his comments on how the eye would have arisen" (Lipson, 1988, p. 6).

So why did Darwin make such claims? It was his grandfather, Erasmus Darwin, in particular who held anti-religious views that had a radical influence on him.

ERASMUS DARWIN

The young Charles Darwin had listened to his grandfather, Erasmus Darwin, since childhood.[11] Actually, it was Erasmus Darwin who first proposed the idea of evolution in England. He was known as a physicist, a psychologist, and a poet, and exercised considerable influence, although he led a dark personal life (Morris, 1989). But Erasmus Darwin was one of the most well-known naturalists in England. Naturalism believed that the essence of the universe lay in nature and that nature had a creative power. While the roots of this doctrine go back to the naturalist philosophy found in ancient Greek and Sumerian myths, its major proponent by the nineteenthth century was the Masonic organization.

The Masons, who adopted naturalism, had their greatest representative in Erasmus Darwin, who was one of the masters of the Canongate Kilwinning Masonic lodge in Edinburgh, Scotland.[12] Additionally, he seems to have been involved to some degree with the Jacobin clubs in France, or with the Illuminati, which were connected with certain Masonic lodges in France and whose primary duty was to oppose religion.[13] Erasmus educated his son Robert (father

---

11. McLean, Glen S., et al, The Evidence for Creation: Examining the Origin of Planet Earth, Springdale: Whitaker House, 1977.
12. Freemasonry Today, Autumn, 1999, Issue 9, p. 5.
13. The "Illuminati" organization established in Bavaria, Germany, in 1776 was a kind of Masonic lodge. The founder of the lodge, Adam Weishaupt (who was of Jewish descent), listed the goals of the organization in this way: 1) The abolishment of all monarchies and methodical governments; 2) the abolishment of personal properties and inheritance; 3) the abolishment of the family and marriage, and the establishment of a communal educational system for children; and 4) the abolishment of all theistic religions. (See Eustace Mullins, The World Order: Our Secret Rulers, p. 5; Lewis Spence, The Encyclopedia of the Occult, p. 223.)

of Charles) to be like himself, and made him a member of Masonic lodges (Morris, 1989). Therefore, Charles Darwin inherited Masonry from his father and grandfather.

The main lines of Darwin's theory were, in reality, determined by his grandfather, whose naturalist works were designed as a guide for Darwin. Erasmus Darwin developed the basic logic that was to give form to Darwinism and expounded on it in books titled *The Temple of Nature* and *Zoonomia*. It was a renewal of the ancient belief that nature has creative power. In 1784 a society was founded to assist in the dissemination (distribution is a better word for clarity) of these ideas—The Philosophical Society—which, decades later, would become one of the largest and most passionate supporters of Charles Darwin's ideas.[14] Darwin's own theory of evolution, however, was first proposed in the Galapagos Islands.

THE GALAPAGOS ISLANDS

Imagine visiting a vibrant green island in the middle of the ocean. On this bit of land, separated from the mainland by a vast ocean, there is a beautiful, rich variety of plants and animals found nowhere else in the world. Living things one never encountered before abound here in great variety. If you found yourself in such a place with this magnificent view in front of you, what would you think?

With such wonderful colors, vitality, and variety before your eyes you would, no doubt, feel a deep sense of pleasure and would ask yourself how all these beautiful things came to be. You may conclude that in the middle of the ocean on a tiny piece of land a great creative artistry is displayed and that everything is part of an extraordinary creation.

However, when Darwin saw this awesome variety in nature, he concluded that every living thing came to be as a result of coincidence. He did not consider that every one of these things was created by the eternal power of God; Darwin's logic led him in the opposite direction.

---

14. Denslow, William R., *10,000 Famous Freemasons*, vol. 1, Richmond, Virginia: Macoy Publishing & Macoy Supply Co., Inc., 1957.

Darwin encountered many living things unseen by most people during his five–year journey, especially on the Galapagos Islands. The Galapagos Islands are a place where there are countless numbers of living species that a scientist may study. In the course of his journey, Darwin paid the most attention to the various kinds of finches, in spite of collecting thousands of living things which he preserved in alcohol.

After examining the physical differences between their beaks, he began to shape his theory. However, recent observations have revealed that the finches did not undergo an unlimited variation as Darwin's theory presupposed. Most of the different types of finches which Darwin thought represented 14 distinct species actually mated with one another, which means that they were variations that belonged to the same species.

Scientific observation shows that the finch beaks, which have been mythicized in almost all evolutionist sources, are in fact an example of "variation"; therefore, they do not constitute evidence for the theory of evolution. For example, Peter and Rosemary Grant, who spent years observing the finch varieties in the Galapagos Islands looking for evidence for evolution, were forced to conclude that "the population, subjected to natural selection, is oscillating back and forth," a fact which implied that no "evolution" that leads to the emergence of new traits ever takes place there.[15] What Darwin really did was to make exaggerated speculations about certain observations he had made. It is true that among finches there has been variation as wide as the gene pool has allowed. Nevertheless, this does not mean that the finch evolved from another bird species or that it can develop into another species. What Darwin saw in the finches was variation; not evidence for evolution.

Modern evolutionists have admitted that claims made by Darwin based on the variation in the beaks of finches are exaggerated

---

15. H. Lisle Gibbs and Peter R. Grant, "Oscillating selection on Darwin's finches," *Nature*, 327, 1987, pp. 513; for more detailed information, please see Jonathan Wells, *Icons of Evolution*, 2000, pp. 159–175.

unscientific suppositions.[16] Indeed, no thinking person can accept inferences made about the origins of every living thing merely on the basis of differences in the beaks of finches. How could that lead to conclusions about the emergence of giant whales, elephants with their distinctive features, flies with their amazing abilities, the magnificent symmetry of the wings of a butterfly, the great variety of fish, crustaceans, birds, reptiles, and most importantly, human beings with intelligence and consciousness?

When a scientist examines living things, variation is not the only aspect to be taken into account. On the contrary, it is evident that a much more important and basic matter is the extraordinary design found in these beings. When dealing with finches, he would consider their flawless flying mechanisms, wings so wonderfully constructed with perfect technology. He would explore the aerodynamic quality of a single feather, its delicate but pliant structure that enables the bird to fly, and the millions of small hooks holding the feathers together. An objective scientist will see the evident truth: this flawless design, matchless beauty, and innumerable variety can only be the work of a Designer. As a result, evolutionists are still unable to resolve Darwin's problem of the "origin of species."

The reason that Darwin and his followers put this reality out of sight is their psychological relationship to atheistic philosophy, a spiritual condition which is clearly perceived in Darwin. His comment on the structure of the eye and the feathers of the peacock is a good example: "I remember well the time when the thought of the eye made me cold all over, but I have got over this stage of complaint and now small trifling particulars of structure often make me very

---

16. It is also now accepted by evolutionist biologists that variations called "microevolution" do not cause "macroevolution"; that is, they do not supply any explanation for the origin of species. The renowned evolutionist paleontologist, Rower Lewin, describes the conclusion reached in a four-day symposium held at Chicago's Field Museum of Natural History in 1980 in these words: "The central question of the Chicago conference was whether the mechanisms underlying microevolution can be extrapolated to explain the phenomena of macroevolution. . . . The answer can be given as a clear 'NO.'"

uncomfortable. The sight of a feather in a peacock's tail, whenever I gaze at it, makes me sick" (Lewin, 1980, p. 883).

This is certainly a demonstration of Darwin's prejudiced point of view toward what he encountered in nature. Because of the great variety of living creatures he observed in the Galapagos Islands, he was content to store them away in alcohol and refused to think about the extraordinary qualities he noticed in them. Yet, one need not go to the Galapagos Islands to see the proofs of distinctive creation throughout the universe. By simply looking at the heavens one can see countless proofs of the signature of God.

The eye, the thought of which once made Darwin cold all over, is just an example of these countless proofs. The eye possesses a structure which is far too complex and perfect to have been the result of chance. It is composed of 40 different components; one of its important aspects is its "irreducible complexity." This means that the eye, to be able to function, must contain every one of these 40 components at once. The eye would be useless if even one component was missing, and every one of these 40 components has its own complex internal design. For example, the retina at the back of the eye is composed of eleven different layers, and one of these layers is a web of blood vessels. This layer, which is the body's densest web of blood vessels, provides the oxygen needed by the cells of the retina to interpret light. Each of the other layers has its own function. No evolutionist can give a convincing answer to the question of how such a complex organ was formed because the eye is one of the signs of the perfect creation of God.

Those who blindly devote themselves to following Darwin and proclaim him as the "lord of the species" must certainly consider what we have said so far about his character. They must see that Darwin's theory depends on a fairytale about the "Temple of Nature" that he learned from his grandfather, on mistaken inferences derived from an amateur's knowledge of biology, on an extreme prejudice for the rejection of creation based on speculations about these mistaken inferences, and on a superficial nineteenth century culture that believed atheism to be science. The only reason why scientific creation is stubbornly ignored is that it is seen as a belief in which God created *Ex nihilo*, or "out of nothing," by His spoken word. Therefore, design shows a Designer, and creation points to a Creator. Consequently, one is held accountable to this Creator. Phillip E. Johnson of Chicago University, who occupies an esteemed position in academic circles despite his criticism of the theory of evolution, explains: "In short, the triumph of Darwinism implied the death of [belief in] God and set the stage for replacing . . . religion with a new faith based on evolutionary naturalism" (Johnson, 1997, p. 99).

In another book Johnson describes this aspect of Darwinism:

> Prejudice is a major problem, however, because the leaders of science see themselves as locked in a desperate battle against religious fundamentalists, a label which they tend to apply broadly to anyone who believes in a Creator who plays an active role in worldly affairs. These fundamentalists are seen as a threat to liberal freedom, and especially as a threat to public support for scientific research. As the creation myth of scientific naturalism, Darwinism plays an indispensable ideological role in the war against fundamentalism. For that reason, the scientific organizations are devoted to protecting Darwinism rather than testing it, and the rules of scientific investigation have been shaped to help them succeed
>
> —Johnson, 1993, p. 155

As we see from this quote, the promotion of Darwinism is one of the most important goals of the evolutionist, not the truth.

THE ORIGIN OF SPECIES

The Origin of Species is regarded in some degree as a "holy" book. However, *The Origin of Species* does more to cause doubt and uncertainty about life's origins. Even Charles Darwin himself had serious reservations about its scientific character. In a letter to his friend, L. Blomefield, he wrote: "So much has been published since the appearance of *The Origin of Species* that I very much doubt whether I retain power of mind and strength to reduce the mass into a digested whole. . . ."[17]

Concerning the contents of the book, one of Darwin's closest friends, A. Sedgwick, replied: "I have read your book with more pain than pleasure. Parts of it I admired greatly, parts I laughed at till my sides were almost sore; other parts I read with absolute sorrow because I think them utterly false and grievously mischievous. Many of your wide conclusions are based upon assumptions which can neither be proved nor disproved. . . . You write of 'natural selection' as if it were done curiously by the selecting agent."[18]

Despite the fact that the book was based on many errors in suppositions and on improvable assertions, today it remains generally unchallenged. Because *The Origin of Species* provides the basic foundation for atheist philosophy, it is regarded as a liberator by ideologies throughout the world that are based on a secular understanding of life. Although most people today have not even read the book, many educational institutions regard it as the basic foundation of modern thought. Jack Barzun describes the importance of *The Origin of Species* in these words: "Clearly, both believers and unbelievers in Natural Selection agreed that Darwinism had succeeded as an orthodoxy, as a rallying point for innumerable, scientific, philosophical, and social movements. Darwin had been the oracle and *The Origin of Species* the 'fixed point with which evolution moved the world.'"[19]

While Darwin and his book continue to receive adulation, Henry M. Morris, in his book *The Long War Against God*, shows how far removed *The Origin of Species* is from science:

In fact, one can search the whole book in vain for any real scientific evidences of evolution. . . . No proof is given anywhere—no examples are cited of new species known to have been produced by natural selection, no transitional forms are shown, no evolutionary mechanisms are documented. Actually, the whole book is

---

17. *The Life and Letters of Charles Darwin,* vol. II, p. 388.
18. Ibid., pp. 42–43.
19. Barzun, Jacques, *Darwin, Marx, Wagner,* Garden City, NY: Doubleday, 1958. p. 69

most notable for its complete lack of documentation. It is all speculation, special pleading, ad hoc assumptions. None of *The Origin's*
evidences or arguments have stood up under modern critical analysis, even by other evolutionists. One can only marvel that such a
book could have had so profound an influence on the subsequent
history of human life and thought. There is bound to be something
more here than meets the eye.

—Morris, 1989, p. 156

As Henry Morris had guessed, there are many different reasons behind the influence that *The Origin of Species* has had on human history. In the whole history of science, no scientific work, whether correct or not, has been adopted with such passion and fanaticism. The
groundbreaking discoveries in the scientific world by Newton and
Einstein were not followed with this kind of zeal. It is not a scientific
conception that is being dealt with here, but a religion that is propa-
gated by the power of suggestion.

BELIEVING THE UNBELIEVABLE

A large number of people believe in religion, but not the Creator God
in the Bible. The main character in Darwinism is "coincidence." No
matter what Darwinist work one reads, one will find mention of the
power of this idol, of its capabilities; experience, and foresight, because Darwinists believe that the universe and everything in it, animate and inanimate, came into being by chance. Coincidence is the
essence and lifeblood of Darwinism. French zoologist Pierre P. Grassé, himself an avid evolutionist, draws attention to this fact: "Chance
becomes a sort of providence, which, under the cover of atheism, is
not named but which is secretly worshipped" (Grassé, 1977, p.107)

The same theme is encountered in other religions as well. In
Greek philosophy, the emergence of living things is also described
with reference to chance occurrences. Ancient Mesopotamian religions worshipped several lifeless idols and believed they were possessed of great powers. According to these cultures, chance—such
as the overflowing of a river or some other natural occurrence—

brought living things into existence. The emergence of new organisms and living species according to Darwinism was also dependent on natural phenomena, like sudden changes in temperature or high levels of radiation.

If coincidence is the main character in evolution, then mutation is the second most important player. Mutation means alterations or changes in the DNA molecule (located in the nucleus of a living cell and carrying genetic information), affected by means of radiation or chemical activity. Mutation usually causes damage that the cell cannot repair. For example, Down syndrome, dwarfism, sickle cell anemia, mental and physical impairments, as well as cancer, are cited as examples of the destructive nature of mutation. Mutation is not something magical that develops beings toward perfection. It is clearly a harmful process that causes death, impairment, and illness. This is recognized by scientists who compare mutation to earthquakes.

While the effects of mutation are always negative, "coincidence" would have you believe it always produces orderly and positive results! And it is believed that this god produces beauty, perfect creatures, and magnificent order. For example, it can create the 100 trillion cells in a human body without error or deficiency. It can create cells like a factory, produce energy, enzymes, and hormones, store information about what it has produced in the information bank of a nucleus. It can distribute raw materials and finished products among different departments with a laboratory and refinery system that analyzes everything coming from outside and a membrane that insures the quality of everything that is released inside. And coincidence always gets it right the first time! For example, coincidence made the life of a living thing dependent on its heart and circulatory system, and in order for the heart to perform its function, created a system of arteries to carry blood to every part of the body; and while it was at it, did not forget a system of veins to carry the blood back to the heart. In the meantime, it added the liver to the system to clean carbon dioxide from the blood, and connected the whole system to the heart. It knew that in order to clean the blood of other impurities, kidneys were needed and so immediately created them.

This list could be extended greatly. For the life of any creature to continue, a large number of organs must perform their function perfectly and at the same time. If even one of them fails to work properly, the creature dies within a few minutes or, at most, a few days. But according to the claims of the evolutionists, coincidence has awareness, bringing into existence millions of complete creatures. It also created human beings as the result of a lengthy process. But not being content just to create human beings, it also conceived of every possible thing that they would need. To provide for the needs of coming generations, it created wheat thousands of years earlier; and for the energy needs of succeeding generations, it created oil. When making the sun a source of energy, it did not neglect to create layers in the atmosphere to protect human beings from its dangerous rays. When designing the human system to breathe, it also created an appropriate atmosphere. It balanced a system that the life of one living thing is dependent on that of another; the existence of oxygen depending on plants, plants on water, water on the atmospheric heat; all these systems depend on the rotation of the Earth which, in turn, depends on the gravitational pull of the heavenly bodies, the distances of the sun and the moon, and thousands of other details. Every creature is nourished by another, and if one becomes extinct, the other is harmed. According to what evolutionists claim, coincidence has such a degree of awareness that is has left out no detail!

Additionally, in the course of time coincidence created millions of living species and adorned each with special characteristics. According to evolutionists, time and chance is such that it can do anything it desires. If it wants to make an eye, it makes it; if it wants to make an arm, it makes that, too. It conceives everything it wants to make and how to make it, obtaining perfect results. Before an eye existed, when there was no such thing as sight, coincidence created two spaces in the skull and inserted two spheres filled with liquid into which light could pass. Later, it set two lenses in the front of this liquid which could easily refract light and project it onto the back wall of the eye. Still later, so the eye could see the surrounding space, it created the optic muscles. But the eye was still unfinished, so it created a retina at the back to perceive light, with nerves connecting it to the brain, tear glands to protect it from drying, and eyelids and eyelashes to protect it from dust and other foreign material. So, evolution formed all these perfect organisms by means of mutation—a process which, under normal circumstances, produces monstrosities, gives rise to defects and diseases, and has no positive effect on living things.

Moreover, evolution also has a special concern for the golden mean ratios and aesthetics of what it creates. Whether animate or inanimate, it takes care that its color, appearance, taste, smell, and shape are aesthetically appropriate. When making a fruit or vegetable, it does so with consideration for its aesthetic as well as its vitamins, minerals, carbohydrates, calories, and sugar content. It is not satisfied to merely make a strawberry but also provides its appealing smell and attractive shape. And of course, it makes a sense of taste and smell in human beings so they may take pleasure from these sensations. The renowned French zoologist Pierre–Paul Grassé says this about the concept: "The opportune appearance of mutations permitting animals and plants to meet their needs seems hard to believe. Yet, the Darwinian Theory is even more demanding: A single plant, a single animal would require thousands and thousands of lucky, appropriate events. Thus, miracles would become the rule: events with an infinitesimal probability could not fail to occur. . . . There is no law against daydreaming, but science must not indulge in it" (Grasse, 1977, p. 103).

So the essence of evolution is based on faith! If human intellect has the capacity to understand that a complex construction cannot form by chance and must be the product of an intelligent plan, then Darwinism is diametrically opposed to human reason. Michael Denton, the famous molecular biologist, describes this interesting situation:

To the skeptic the proposition that the genetic programs of higher organisms, consisting of something close to a 1,000 million bits of information, equivalent to the sequence of letters in a small library of 1,000 volumes, containing in encoded form countless thousands of intricate algorithms controlling, specifying, and ordering the growth and development of billions and billions of cells into the form of a complex organism, were composed by a purely random process is simply an affront to reason. But to the Darwinist, the idea is accepted without a ripple of doubt—the paradigm takes precedence.

—Denton, 1985, p. 351

One will conclude that there is a great similarity between evolution and ancient cultures. Just as idolaters believed that lifeless idols created, evolutionists believe that lifeless matter, prompted by random occurrences, created living things, including themselves. So the religion of Darwinism is founded on an illusion. However, even its founder, Charles Darwin, was aware that complex living things could not have come into being by chance. The perfect order in nature showed him that every existing thing was possessed of a magnificent design. Darwin acknowledged his doubts in these words:

I cannot anyhow be contented to view this wonderful universe, and especially the nature of man. . . . I am inclined to look at everything as resulting from designed laws. . . . All these laws may have been expressly designed by an omniscient Creator, who foresaw every future event and consequence. But the more I think, the more bewildered I become.[20]

I am conscious that I am in an utterly hopeless muddle. I cannot think that the world, as we see it, is the result of chance; and yet I cannot look at each separate thing as the result of Design.[21]

I could give many most striking and curious illustrations in all [living] classes; so many that I think it cannot be chance.[22]

---

20. *The Life and Letters of Charles Darwin,* vol. II, p. 105.
21. Ibid., p. 146.
22. Ibid., vol. I, p. 455.

CHAPTER 5

THE IMPACT OF THE DARWINISM

The suggestion Darwinism gives to people is, "You are not responsible to anyone because you owe your life to chance. In the struggle to survive you may have to crush others; this world is a world of conflict and self–interest." It is the message given by biological concepts of Darwinism such as "natural selection," "random mutation," "struggle for survival," "survival of the fittest," etc.

To be an evolutionist it is necessary to believe that living beings were formed from lifeless matter, that reptiles began to fly as a result of a coincidental process, that highly complex organisms such as cells, and eventually eyes and ears, came into existence by random chance. Sea creatures such as whales evolved from mammals like bears that went into the sea in search of food. Dinosaurs that ran after flies developed wings and became birds.

It is evident how unreasonable and illogical these presuppositions are. One who reads these words might think that since respected scientists believe these things, they must have proof. But there is not the slightest proof—only guesses, suppositions, probabilities, and whims. The decision about these things has already been made; now it is necessary only to believe.

All that is needed to get people to believe in this faith is a single article in a magazine, a book, or a short documentary film. Even if a scientist wishes, they cannot ask questions which would contradict the Darwinian theory. Those who do so may be ostracized and excluded from academia. In fact, they are "black–balled" in most cases.

Anyone with minimal scientific knowledge knows that there would not be enough time for a fish coming onto the land to grow accustomed to the new environment, and that it would soon die. Anyone who has studied the complex structure of a cell will understand that this miraculous organism could not have come to be through coincidence. They will realize that a reptile cannot just develop wings by chance and fly. Perceived with a common sense approach, such facts will be proven by every kind of experiment and observation.

But people whose minds have been clouded by Darwinist doctrine do not want to think about such things; they are afraid to think about them. However, it is only by thinking, investigating, and observing that a person will be able to see the truth and overcome taboos. In order to understand that God created the universe, all one has to do is look at the signature of God in the creation. Psalm 19:1 says, "The heavens declare the glory of God; and the firmament sheweth his handywork." Again in Psalms 97:6: "The heavens declare his righteousness, and all the people see his glory." When one frees himself of the evolutionary mindset, the only conclusion he can come to is that there is a supreme Creator.

Darwinist leaders are aware that freedom of thought will mean the end to their theory of evolution, and for this reason they have discouraged thought in academia and public schools. The method they use is to suggest to people that aspects of science are highly complex and very difficult to understand. They use incomprehensible terminology, Latin words, and scientific comparisons, and insist that such things can never be understood by ordinary people.

People are thus persuaded and decide from the beginning that they cannot understand and that the fundamentals of Darwinism can be comprehended only by great men of science. In order to avoid embarrassment, the most logical thing, as they see it, is to accept what Darwinist leaders say. So between the leaders of academia and the followers, a hierarchy has been established and everyone knows their place.

But despite all these precautions, evolutionists cannot prevent their advocates from experiencing doubt because their surroundings provide thousands of proofs for creation. In order to doubt the

Darwinist theories it is enough to contemplate the perfect order of the world; the interesting characteristics of every living thing, the dazzling precision in the whole of creation from an atom to the galaxies, the complex structure of every living organism, the beauties of nature, the smell of a rose, or the taste of a fruit. Satan himself knows that the sun is not a god to be worshipped, that God created the sun just as He created the whole universe. Darwinism diverts people from belief in God. In fact, there is no "evolutionary process" to study. That is why one of its most renowned supporters, Julian Huxley, described the purpose of the theory of evolution in these terms: "A religion is essentially an attitude to the world as a whole. Thus evolution, for example, may prove as powerful a principle to coordinate man's beliefs and hopes as God was in the past" (Huxley and Bronowski, 1968, p. 99).

The most important aim of the theory is to graft into the human mind the deception that the world was not created by God and that consequently there is no responsibility for adhering to a divine Creator. Evolutionists emphasize this often, pointing out that a human being is his own "master" and responsible only to himself. The truth is God created man for His own purpose, to have fellowship with Him. It is our choice to know Him and experience an intimate personal relationship with the Creator of the universe.

CHAPTER 6

THE DILEMMA OF DARWINISM

E volutionists theorize that two formulas can enable everything to make itself—with the exception of man–made things, such as automobiles or buildings. Complicated things, such as wooden boxes with nails in them, require thought, intelligence, and careful workmanship. But everything else about us, such as our DNA sequencing in genetic biology, is declared to be the result of accidental mishaps, random confusion, and time. You will not even need raw materials to begin with. They make themselves, too. Here is the evolutionary formula for making a universe: nothing + nothing = two elements + time = 92 natural elements + time = all physical laws and a completely structured universe of galaxies, systems, stars, planets, and moons orbiting in perfect balance and order. This is the evolutionary formula for making life: dirt + water + time = living creatures.

18TH AND 19TH CENTURY SCIENTISTS

Prior to the middle of the 1800s, scientists were researchers who firmly believed that all nature was made by a Master Designer. Those pioneers who laid the foundations of modern science were creationists. They were men of giant intellect who struggled against great odds in carrying on their work. They were hardworking researchers. In contrast, the philosophers sat around hardly stirring from their armchairs and theorized about everything while the scientists, ignoring them, kept at their work.

But a change came about in the nineteenth century, when the

philosophers tried to gain control of scientific endeavor and suppress research and findings that would be unfavorable to their theories. Today's evolutionists vigorously defend the unscientific theories they thought up over a century ago.

FACT:
EVOLUTIONARY THEORY WAS DESTROYED BY SEVEN SCIENTIFIC RESEARCH FINDINGS—BEFORE DARWIN PUBLISHED HIS THEORY.

William Paley (1743–1805), in his 1802 classic *Natural Theology,* summarized the viewpoint of the scientists. He argued that the kind of carefully designed structures we see in the living world point clearly to a Designer. If we see a watch, we know that it had a designer and maker; it would be foolish to imagine that it made itself. This is the "argument by design." All about us is the world of nature, and over our heads at night is a universe of stars. We can ignore or ridicule what is there or say it all made itself, but our scoffing does not change the reality of the situation. A leading atheistic scientist of our time, Fred Hoyle, wrote that "although it was not difficult to disprove Darwinism, what Paley had to say appeared likely to be unanswerable" (Hoyle and Wickramasinghe, 1981, p. 96).

Carl Linn (Carolus Linnaeus, 1707–1778) was a scientist who classified immense numbers of living organisms. An earnest creationist, he clearly saw that there were no halfway species. All plant and animal species were definite categories, separate from one another. Variation was possible within a species, and there were many subspecies. But there were no crossovers from one species to another (Milner, 1990).

First Law of Thermodynamics (1847)—Heinrich von Helmholtz stated the *law of conservation of energy*: the sum total of all matter will always remain the same. This law refutes several aspects of evolutionary theory. Isaac Asimov calls it "the most fundamental generalization about the universe that scientists have ever been able to make" (Asimov, 1970, p. 6).

Second Law of Thermodynamics (1850)—R. J. E. Clausius stated

the *law of entropy:* all systems will tend toward the most mathemati-
cally probable state and eventually become totally random and dis-
organized. In other words, everything runs down, wears out, and
goes to pieces. This law totally eliminates the basic evolutionary
theory that simplicity evolves into complex life forms. Even Albert
Einstein was intrigued about this law. [23]

Gregor Mendel (1822–1884) was a creationist who lived and
worked near Brunn (now Brno), Czechoslovakia. He was a science
and math teacher. Unlike the theorists, Mendel was a true scientist.
He bred garden peas and studied the results of crossing various varieties. Beginning his work in 1856, he concluded it within eight years.
In 1865, he reported his research in the *Journal of the Brunn Society
for the Study of Natural Science.* The journal was distributed to 120
libraries in Europe, England, and America. Yet his research was totally ignored by the scientific community until it was rediscovered in
1900.[24] His experiments clearly showed that one species could not
transmute into another one. A genetic barrier existed that could not
be bridged. Mendel's work laid the basis for modern genetics, and
his discoveries effectively destroyed the basis for species evolution.[25]

Louis Pasteur (1822–1895) was another genuine scientist. In
the process of studying fermentation, he performed his famous
1861 experiment, in which he disproved the theory of spontaneous
generation. Life cannot arise from non–living materials. This experiment was very important, for, up to that time, a majority of scientists
believed in spontaneous generation. They thought that if a pile of
old clothes were left in a corner, it would breed mice! The proof was
that, upon later returning to the clothes, mice would frequently be
found there. Pasteur concluded from his experiment that only God
could create living creatures. But modern evolutionary theory continues to be based on that outdated theory disproved by Pasteur:
spontaneous generation (life arises from non–life). Why? Because it

23. Rifkin, Jeremy, *Entropy: A New World View,* 1980.
24. Fisher, R. A., "Has Mendel's Work Been Rediscovered?" *Annals of Science,*
Vol. 1, No. 2, 1936.
25. Pitman, Michael, *Adam and Evolution,* 1984 .

is the only basis on which evolution could occur. As Adams notes, "With spontaneous generation discredited [by Pasteur], biologists were left with no theory of the origin of life at all."[26]

August Friedrich Leopold Weismann (1834–1914) was a German biologist who disproved Lamarck's notion of "the inheritance of acquired characteristics." He is primarily remembered as the scientist who cut off the tails of 901 young white mice in 19 successive generations; yet each new generation was born with a full–length tail. The final generation, he reported, had tails as long as those originally measured on the first. Weismann also carried out other experiments that buttressed his refutation of Lamarckism. His discoveries, along with the fact that circumcision of Jewish males for 4,000 years had not affected the foreskin, doomed the theory.[27] Yet Lamarckism continues today as the disguised basis of evolutionary biology. For example, evolutionists still teach that giraffes kept stretching their necks to reach higher branches, so their necks became longer! In a later book, Darwin abandoned natural selection as unworkable, and returned to Lamarckism as the cause of the never–observed change from one species to another.[28]

Here is a brief, partial overview of what scientists were accomplishing in the eighteenth and nineteenth centuries. All of them were creationists:

1. *Louis Agassiz* (1807–1873): glacial geology, ichthyology
2. *Charles Babbage* (1792–1871): actuarial tables, calculating machine, foundations of computer science
3. *Francis Bacon* (1561–1626): scientific method of research
4. *Robert Boyle* (1627–1691): chemistry, gas dynamics
5. *Sir David Brewster* (1781–1868): optical mineralogy, kaleidoscope
6. *Georges Cuvier* (1769–1832): comparative anatomy, vertebrate paleontology

---

26. Adams, J. Edison, *Plants: An Introduction to Modern Biology*, 1967, p. 585.
27. Rostand, Jean, *Orion Book of Evolution*, 1960.
28. Hedtke, Randall, *The Secret of the Sixth Edition*, 1984.

7. *Sir Humphry Davy* (1778-1829): thermokinetics
8. *Jean Henri Fabre* (1823-1915): entomology of living insects
9. *Michael Faraday* (1791-1867): electric generator, electro–magnetics, field theory
10. *Sir John A. Fleming* (1849-1945): electronics, thermic valve
11. *Joseph Henry* (1797-1878): electric motor, galvanometer
12. *Sir William Herschel* (1738-1822): galactic astronomy, double stars
13. *James Joule* (1818-1889): reversible thermodynamics
14. *Lord William Kelvin* (1824-1907): absolute temperature scale, energetics, thermodynamics, transatlantic cable
15. *Johannes Kepler* (1571-1630): celestial mechanics, ephemeris tables, physical astronomy
16. *Carolus Linnaeus* (1707-1778): classification system, systematic biology
17. *Joseph Lister* (1827-1912): antiseptic surgery
18. *Matthew Maury* (1806-1873): hydrography, oceanography
19. *James C. Maxwell* (1831-1879): electrical dynamics, statistical thermodynamics
20. *Gregor Mendel* (1822-1884): genetics
21. *Samuel F. B. Morse* (1791-1872): telegraph
22. *Isaac Newton* (1642-1727): calculus, dynamics, law of gravity, reflecting telescopes
23. *Blaise Pascal* (1623-1662): hydrostatics, barometer
24. *Louise Pasteur* (1822-1895): bacteriology, biogenesis law, pasteurization, vaccination, and immunization
25. *Sir William Ramsey* (1852-1916): inert gases, isotropic chemistry
26. *John Ray* (1627-1705): natural history, classification of plants and animals
27. *John Rayleigh* (1842-1919): dimensional analysis, model analysis
28. *Bernhard Riemann* (1826-1866): non–Euclidean geometry
29. *Sir James Simpson* (1811-1870): chloroform, gynecology
30. *Sir George Stokes* (1819-1903): fluid mechanics
31. *Rudolph Virchow* (1821-1902): pathology

Eighteenth and nineteenth century contributions to science by evolutionists:

1. *Emmanuel Swedenborg* (1688–1772) was a do–nothing expert. In his 1734 book, *Principia,* he theorized that a rapidly rotating nebula formed itself into our solar system of sun and planets. He claimed that he obtained the idea from spirits during a séance. It is significant that the nebular hypothesis theory originated from such a source.

2. *Comte de Buffon* (1707–1788) was a dissolute philosopher who, unable to improve on the work of Linnaeus, spent his time criticizing him. He theorized that species originated from one another and that a chunk was torn out of the sun, which became our planet. As with the other philosophers, he presented no evidence in support of his theories.

3. *Jean–Baptist Lamarck* (1744–1829) made a name for himself by theorizing. He accomplished little else of significance. He laid the foundation of modern evolutionary theory with his concept of "inheritance of acquired characteristics," which was later given the name *Lamarckism.* In 1809 he published a book, *Philosophie Zoologique,* in which he declared that the giraffe got its long neck by stretching it up to reach the higher branches and birds that lived in water grew webbed feet. According to that, if you pull hard on your feet, you will gradually increase their length; and, if you decide in your mind to do so, you can grow hair on your bald head, and your offspring will never be bald. This is science? Lamarck's other erroneous contribution to evolution was the theory of *uniformitarianism.* This is the conjecture that all earlier ages on Earth were exactly as they are today, calm and peaceful with no worldwide flood or other great catastrophes.

4. *Robert Chambers* (1802–1883) was a spiritualist who regularly communicated with spirits. As a result of his contacts, he wrote the first popular evolution book in all of Britain. Called *Vestiges of Creation* (1844), it was printed 15 years before Charles Darwin's book, *The Origin of Species.*

5. *Charles Lyell* (1797–1875). Like Charles Darwin, Lyell inherited

great wealth and was able to spend his time theorizing. Lyell published his *Principles of Geology* in 1830–1833 and it became the basis for the modern theory of sedimentary strata—even though twentieth–century discoveries in radiocarbon dating, missing strata, and overthrusts (older strata on top of more recent strata) have nullified the theory. In order to prove his theory, Lyell was quite willing to misstate the facts. He learned that Niagara Falls had eroded a seven–mile [11 km] channel from Queenston, Ontario, and that it was eroding at about three feet [1 m] a year. So Lyell conveniently changed that to one foot [.3 m] a year, which meant that the falls had been flowing for 35,000 years! But Lyell had not told the truth. Three feet of erosion a year, at its present rate of flow, would only take us back 7,000 to 9,000 years. It would be expected that, just after the flood, the flow would, for a time, have greatly increased the erosion rate. Lyell was a close friend of Darwin, and urged him to write his book, *The Origin of Species.*

6. *Alfred Russell Wallace* (1823–1913) is considered to be the man who developed the theory which Darwin published. Wallace was deeply involved in spiritism at the time he formulated the theory in his *Ternate Paper.* Darwin, with the help of two friends, Charles Lyell and Joseph Hooker, pirated and published the paper under his own name. Darwin, a wealthy man, thus obtained the royalties which belonged to Wallace, a poverty–ridden theorist. In 1980, Arnold C. Brackman, in his book *A Delicate Arrangement,* established that Darwin plagiarized Wallace's material. It was arranged that a paper by Darwin would be read to the Royal Society in London while Wallace's was held back until later. Priorities for the ideas thus having been taken care of, Darwin set to work to prepare his book. In 1875, Wallace came out openly for spiritism and Marxism, another stepchild of Darwinism. It is of interest to note that after engaging in spiritism, certain men in history have been seized with a deep hatred of God. They have then been guided to devise evil teachings that have destroyed large numbers of people, while others have engaged in warfare which has annihilated millions. In connection with this, we think

of such known spiritists as Sigmund Freud and Adolf Hitler. Wallace's theory that species have changed in the past, one species descended from another in a manner that we cannot prove today, is exactly what modern evolution teaches. Yet there is no more evidence supporting the theory today than Wallace had in 1858, when he devised the theory.

In February 1858, while in a delirious fever on the island of Ternate in the Molaccas, Wallace conceived the idea "survival of the fittest" as being the method by which species change. But the concept proves nothing. The fittest; which one is that? It is the one that survives the longest. Which one survives longest? The fittest. This is circular reasoning. The phrase says nothing about the evolutionary process, much less proving it.

In the first edition of his book, Darwin regarded "natural selection" and "survival of the fittest" as different concepts. By the sixth edition of his *The Origin of Species,* he thought they meant the same thing, but that "survival of the fittest" was the more accurate. In a still later book (*Descent of Man,* 1871), Darwin ultimately abandoned "natural selection" as a hopeless mechanism and returned to Lamarckism. Even Darwin recognized the theory was falling to pieces. The supporting evidence just was not there.

7. *Charles Darwin* (1809–1882) was born into wealth and able to have a life of ease. He took two years of medical school at Edinburgh University, and then dropped out. It was the only scientific training he ever received. Because he spent the time in bars with his friends, he barely passed his courses. Darwin had no particular purpose in life, and his father planned to get him into a nicely paid job as an Anglican minister. Darwin did not object. But, instead, an influential relative got him a position as the unpaid "naturalist" on a ship planning to sail around the world, the *Beagle.* The voyage lasted from December 1831 to October 1836.

It is not commonly known that Charles Darwin, while a naturalist aboard the *Beagle*, was initiated into witchcraft in South America by nationals. During horseback travels into the interior, he took part in their ceremonies and, as a result, something happened to him. Upon his return to England, his health was strangely weakened and he spent the rest of his life working on theories to destroy faith in the Creator.

After leaving South America, Darwin went to the Galapagos Islands for a few days. While there, he saw some finches which had blown in from South America and adapted to their environment, producing several subspecies. He was certain that this showed cross-species evolution (change into new species). But they were still finches. This theory about the finches was the primary evidence of evolution he brought back with him to England. Yet the birds were all essentially alike, and consisted of subspecies of an original pair.

Darwin, never a scientist and knowing nothing about the practicalities of genetics, then married his first cousin, which resulted in all seven of his children having physical or mental disorders. (One girl died after birth, another at ten. His oldest daughter had a prolonged breakdown at 15. Three of his children became semi-invalids, and his last son was born mentally retarded and died 19 months after birth.)

His book, *The Origin of Species*, was first published in November 1859. The full title, *On the Origin of Species by Means of Natural Selection or the Preservation of Favoured Races in the Struggle for Life*, reveals the viciousness of the underlying concept; this concept led directly to two of the worst wars in the history of mankind. Darwin's book had what some men wanted: a clear out-in-the-open, current statement in favor of species change.

So, in spite of its laughable imperfections, they capitalized on it. Here is what you will find in his book:

» Darwin would cite authorities that he did not mention. He repeatedly said it was "only an abstract," and "a fuller edition" would come out later. But, although he wrote other books, try as he may he never could find the proof for his theories. No one since has found it either.

» When he did name an authority, it was just an opinion from a letter. Phrases indicating the hypothetical nature of his ideas were frequent: "it might have been," "maybe," "probably," "it is conceivable that." A favorite of his was: "Let us take an imaginary example."

» Darwin would suggest a possibility, and later refer back to it as a fact: "As we have already demonstrated previously." Elsewhere he would suggest a possible series of events and then conclude by assuming that proved the point.

» He relied heavily on stories instead of facts. Confusing examples would be given. He would use specious and devious arguments, and spent much time suggesting possible explanations why the facts he needed were not available.

Here is an example of his reasoning. To explain the fossil trans–species gaps, Darwin suggested that species must have been changing quickly in other parts of the world where men had not yet examined the strata. Later these changed species traveled over to the western world, to be found in strata there as new species. So species were changing on the other side of the world, and that was why species in the process of change were not found on our side!

With thinking like this, who needs science? But remember that Charles Darwin had very little science instruction. Here is Darwin's explanation of how one species changes into another. It is a variation of Lamarck's theory of inheritance of acquired characteristics.[29] Calling it *pangenesis*, Darwin said that an organ affected by the environment would respond by giving off particles that he called *gemmules*. These particles supposedly helped determine hereditary characteristics. The environment would affect an organ, gemmules would drop out of the organ, and the gemmules would travel to the reproductive organs, where they would affect the cells.[30] In his book, Darwin taught that man came from an ape, and that the stronger races would, within a century or two, destroy the weaker ones.

After taking part in the witchcraft ceremonies, not only was his

---

29. Nicholas Hutton III, *Evidence of Evolution,* 1962
30. W. Stansfield, *Science of Evolution,* 1977

mind affected but his body was also. He developed a chronic and incapacitating illness and went to his death under a depression he could not shake. He frequently commented in private letters that he recognized that there was no evidence for his theory, and that it could destroy the morality of the human race. He stated, "Long before the reader has arrived at this part of my work, a crowd of difficulties will have occurred to him. Some of them are so serious that to this day I can hardly reflect on them without in some degree becoming staggered".[31]

Another subject that posed a quandary for Darwin's theory was inheritance. At the time when Darwin developed his theory, the question of how living beings transmitted their traits to other generations—that is, how inheritance took place—was not completely understood. That is why the naïve belief that inheritance was transmitted through blood was commonly accepted.

Vague beliefs about inheritance led Darwin to base his theory on completely false grounds. Darwin assumed that natural selection was the "mechanism of evolution." Yet one question remained unanswered: How would these "useful traits" be selected and transmitted from one generation to the next? At this point, Darwin embraced the Lamarckian theory, that is, "the inheritance of acquired traits." In his book, *The Great Evolution Mystery,* Gordon R. Taylor, a researcher advocating the theory of evolution, expresses the view that Darwin was heavily influenced by Lamarck:

> Lamarckism . . . is known as the inheritance of acquired characteristics. . . . Darwin himself, as a matter of fact, was inclined to believe that such inheritance occurred and cited the reported case of a man who had lost his fingers and bred sons without fingers. . . . [Darwin] had not, he said, gained a single idea from Lamarck. This was doubly ironical, for Darwin repeatedly toyed with the idea of the inheritance of acquired characteristics and, if it is so dreadful, it is Darwin who should be denigrated rather than Lamarck. . . . In

---

31. Charles Darwin, *The Origin of Species,* 1860, p.178; quoted from Harvard Classics, 1909 ed., Vol. 11

the 1859 edition of his work, Darwin refers to "changes of external conditions" causing variation but subsequently these conditions are described as directing variation and cooperating with natural selection in directing it.... Every year he attributed more and more to the agency of use or disuse.... By 1868 when he published *Varieties of Animals and Plants under Domestication* he gave a whole series of examples of supposed Lamarckian inheritance: such as a man losing part of his little finger and all his sons being born with deformed little fingers, and boys born with foreskins much reduced in length as a result of generations of circumcision.[32]

However, Lamarck's thesis, as we have seen above, was disproved by the laws of genetic inheritance discovered by the Austrian monk and botanist Gregor Mendel. The concept of "useful traits" was therefore left unsupported. Genetic laws show that acquired traits are not passed on, and that genetic inheritance takes place according to certain unchanging laws. These laws support the view that species remain unchanged. No matter how many cows breed, the species itself will never change. Cows will always be cows.

Gregor Mendel announced the laws of genetic inheritance in a scientific paper published in 1865, laws that he discovered as a result of long experiment and observation. But this paper didn't attract the attention of the scientific world until toward the end of the century. By the beginning of the twentieth century, the truth of these laws had been accepted by the whole scientific community. This was a serious dead-end for Darwin's theory, which tried to base the concept of "useful traits" on Lamarck.

Here we must correct a general misapprehension: Mendel opposed not only Lamarck's model of evolution, but also Darwin's. As the article "Mendel's Opposition to Evolution and to Darwin," published in the *Journal of Heredity,* makes clear, "he [Mendel] was familiar with *The Origin of Species* . . . and he was opposed to Darwin's theory; Darwin was arguing for descent with modification through

---

32. Gordon Rattray Taylor, *The Great Evolution Mystery,* London: Abacus, 1984, pp. 36–41

natural selection, Mendel was in favor of the orthodox doctrine of special creation."[33]

The laws discovered by Mendel put Darwinism in a very difficult position. For these reasons, scientists who supported Darwinism tried to develop a different model of evolution in the first quarter of the twentieth century. Thus was born "neo–Darwinism."

Neo–Darwinism

A group of scientists who were determined to reconcile Darwinism with the science of genetics came together at a meeting organized by the Geological Society of America in 1941. After long discussion, they agreed on ways to create a new interpretation of Darwinism and over the next few years, specialists produced a synthesis of their fields into a revised theory of evolution.

The scientists who participated in establishing the new theory included the geneticists G. Ledyard Stebbins and Theodosius Dobzhansky, the zoologists Ernst Mayr and Julian Huxley, the paleontologists George Gaylord Simpson and Glenn L. Jepsen, and the mathematical geneticists Sir Ronald A. Fisher and Sewall Wright (Denton, 1985).

To counter the fact of "genetic stability" (genetic homeostasis), this group of scientists employed the concept of "mutation," which had been proposed by the Dutch botanist Hugo de Vries at the beginning of the twentieth century. Mutations were defects that occurred, for unknown reasons, in the inheritance mechanism of living things. Organisms undergoing mutation developed some unusual structures, which deviated from the genetic information they inherited from their parents. The concept of "random mutation" was supposed to explain the advantageous variations which, according to Darwin, allowed living organisms to evolve, a phenomenon that Darwin himself was unable to explain, but simply tried to sidestep by referring to Lamarck. The Geological Society of America group named this new theory, which was formulated by adding the concept of mutation to

33. B. E. Bishop, "Mendel's Opposition to Evolution and to Darwin," *Journal of Heredity* 87 (1996)

Darwin's natural selection thesis, the "synthetic theory of evolution" or the "modern synthesis." In a short time, this theory came to be known as "neo-Darwinism" and its supporters as "neo-Darwinists."

Yet there was a serious problem. While it was true that mutations changed the genetic data of living organisms, this change always occurred to the detriment of the living thing concerned. All observed mutations ended up with disfigured, weak, or diseased individuals and, sometimes, led to the death of the organism. Hence, in an attempt to find examples of "useful mutations" which improve the genetic data in living organisms, neo-Darwinists conducted many experiments and observations. For decades they conducted mutation experiments on fruit flies and various other species. However, in none of these experiments could a mutation which improved the genetic data of a living being be seen.

Today the issue of mutation is still a great impasse for Darwinism. Despite the fact that the theory of natural selection considers mutations to be the unique source of "useful changes," no mutations of any kind have been observed that are actually useful (that is, that improve the genetic information).

Another impasse for neo-Darwinists came from the fossil record. Even in Darwin's time, fossils were already posing an important obstacle to the theory. While Darwin himself accepted the lack of fossils of "intermediate species," he also predicted that further research would provide evidence of these lost transitional forms. However, despite all the paleontologists' efforts, the fossil record continued to remain a serious obstacle to the theory.

CHAPTER 7

THE FOSSIL RECORD

The evolutionist assertion is that each species on Earth came from a single common ancestor through minor changes. In other words, the theory considers life as a continuous phenomenon, without any preordained or fixed categories. However, the observation of nature clearly does not reveal such a continuous picture. What emerges from the living world is that life forms are strictly separated into very distinct categories. Robert Carroll, an evolutionist authority, admits this fact in his *Patterns and Processes of Vertebrate Evolution:* "Although an almost incomprehensible number of species inhabit Earth today, they do not form a continuous spectrum of barely distinguishable intermediates. Instead, nearly all species can be recognized as belonging to a relatively limited number of clearly distinct major groups, with very few illustrating intermediate structures or ways of life."[34]

Therefore, evolutionists assume that "intermediate" life forms that constitute links between living organisms did live in the past. That is why paleontology, the science of the study of fossils, is considered the fundamental and most important branch of science that can shed light on the origin of life on Earth. Evolution is alleged to be a process that took place in the past, and the only scientific source that can provide us with information on the history of life is fossil discoveries. The well-known French paleontologist Pierre-Paul Grassé has this to say on the subject: "Naturalists must remember

---

34. Carroll, Robert L., *Patterns and Processes of Vertebrate Evolution,* Cambridge University Press, 1997, p. 9.

that the process of evolution is revealed only through fossil forms. . . . [O]nly paleontology can provide them with the evidence of evolution and reveal its course or mechanisms" (Grasse, 1977, p. 82).

Fossil beds, studied with great intensity for the last 200 years, reveal a picture totally at odds with Darwin's theory. Species did not emerge through small cumulative changes; they appeared quite suddenly and fully-formed. In order for the fossil record to shed any light on the subject, we will need to compare the theory of evolution with fossil discoveries.

According to the theory of evolution, every species has emerged from a predecessor. One species which existed previously turned into something else over time and all species have come into being in this way. According to this theory, the transformation proceeds gradually over millions of years.

If this were the case, then innumerable intermediate species should have lived during the immense period of time when these transformations were supposedly occurring. For instance, there should have lived in the past some half–fish/half–reptile creatures which had acquired some reptilian traits in addition to the fish traits they already had. Or there should have been some reptile/bird creatures which had acquired some avian traits in addition to the reptilian traits they already possessed. Evolutionists refer to these imaginary creatures, which they believe to have lived in the past, as "transitional forms."

If such animals had really existed, there would have been millions, even billions, of them. More importantly, the remains of these creatures should be present in the fossil record. The number of these transitional forms should have been even greater than that of present animal species, and their remains should be found all over the world. In *The Origin of Species*, Darwin accepted this fact and explained: "If my theory be true, numberless intermediate varieties, linking most closely all of the species of the same group together must assuredly have existed. . . . Consequently evidence of their former existence could be found only amongst fossil remains" (Darwin, 1964, p. 179).

Even Darwin himself was aware of the absence of such transitional forms. He hoped that they would be found in the future.

Despite his optimism, he realized that these missing intermediate forms were the biggest stumbling-block for his theory. That is why he wrote the following in the chapter of *The Origin of Species* entitled "Difficulties on Theory": ". . . Why, if species have descended from other species by fine gradations, do we not everywhere see innumerable transitional forms? Why is not all nature in confusion, instead of the species being, as we see them, well defined? . . . But, as by this theory innumerable transitional forms must have existed, why do we not find them embedded in countless numbers in the crust of the earth? . . . But in the intermediate region, having intermediate conditions of life, why do we not now find closely-linking intermediate varieties? This difficulty for a long time quite confounded me."[35]

The only explanation Darwin could come up with to counter this objection was the argument that the fossil record uncovered so far was inadequate. He asserted that when the fossil record had been studied in detail, the missing links would be found.

Believing in Darwin's prophecy, evolutionary paleontologists have been digging up fossils and searching for missing links all over the world since the middle of the nineteenth century. Despite their best efforts, no transitional forms have yet been uncovered. All the fossils unearthed in excavations have shown that, contrary to the beliefs of evolutionists, life appeared on Earth all of a sudden and fully-formed. Robert Carroll, an expert on vertebrate paleontology and a committed evolutionist, comes to admit that the Darwinist hope has not been satisfied with fossil discoveries. Despite more than 100 years of intense collecting efforts since the time of Darwin's death, the fossil record still does not yield the picture of infinitely numerous transitional links that he expected.[36]

Another evolutionary paleontologist, K. S. Thomson, tells us that new groups of organisms appear very abruptly in the fossil record: "When a major group of organisms arises and first appears in the re-

---

35. Darwin, Charles, *The Origin of Species by Means of Natural Selection,* New York: The Modern Library, 1993, pp. 124–125.
36. Carroll, Robert L., *Patterns and Processes of Vertebrate Evolution,* Cambridge University Press, 1997, p. 25.

cord, it seems to come fully equipped with a suite of new characters not seen in related, putatively ancestral groups. These radical changes in morphology and function appear to arise very quickly. . . ."[37]

Biologist Francis Hitching, in his book *The Neck of the Giraffe: Where Darwin Went Wrong*, states:

> If we find fossils, and if Darwin's theory was right, we can predict what the rock should contain; finely graduated fossils leading from one group of creatures to another group of creatures at a higher level of complexity. The "minor improvements" in successive generations should be as readily preserved as the species themselves. But this is hardly ever the case. In fact, the opposite holds true, as Darwin himself complained; "innumerable transitional forms must have existed, but why do we not find them embedded in countless numbers in the crust of the earth?" Darwin felt though that the "extreme imperfection" of the fossil record was simply a matter of digging up more fossils. But as more and more fossils were dug up, it was found that almost all of them, without exception, were very close to current living animals.[38]

The fossil record reveals that species emerged suddenly with totally different structures and remained exactly the same over the longest geological periods. Stephen Jay Gould, a Harvard University paleontologist and well-known evolutionist, admitted this fact first in the late '70s: "The history of most fossil species include two features particularly inconsistent with gradualism: 1) Stasis—most species exhibit no directional change during their tenure on Earth. They appear in the fossil record looking much the same as when they disappear; morphological change is usually limited and directionless; 2) Sudden appearance—in any local area, a species does not arise gradually by the steady transformation of its ancestors; it appears all at once and 'fully formed.'"[39]

---

37. Thomson, K. S., *Morphogenesis and Evolution*, Oxford, Oxford University Press, 1988, p. 98.
38. Hitching, Francis, *The Neck of the Giraffe: Where Darwin Went Wrong*, Tichnor and Fields, New Haven, 1982, p. 40.
39. Gould, S. J., "Evolution's Erratic Pace," *Natural History*, vol. 86, May 1977.

Further research only strengthened the facts of stasis and sudden appearance. Stephen Jay Gould and Niles Eldredge write in 1993 that "most species, during their geological history, either do not change in any appreciable way, or else they fluctuate mildly in morphology, with no apparent direction."[40]

Robert Carroll is forced to agree in 1997 that "most major groups appear to originate and diversify over geologically very short durations, and to persist for much longer periods without major morphological or trophic change."[41]

At this point, it is necessary to clarify just what the concept of "transitional form" means. The intermediate forms predicted by the theory of evolution are living things falling between two species, but which possess deficient or semi-developed organs. Sometimes the concept of an intermediate form is misunderstood, and living structures are seen as possessing the features of transitional forms when they don't. For instance, if one group of living things possesses features which belong to another, this is not an intermediate form feature. The platypus, a mammal living in Australia, reproduces by laying eggs just like reptiles. In addition, it has a bill similar to that of a duck. Scientists describe such creatures as the platypus as "mosaic creatures." That mosaic creatures do not count as intermediate forms is also accepted by foremost paleontologists such as Stephen Jay Gould and Niles Eldredge.[42]

Fossil remains provide evolutionists with their only real hope of finding evidence that evolution might have occurred in the past. If the fossils do not witness to evolution in the past, then it could not be occurring now either. There is absolutely no indication from the fossil record that evolution has ever occurred on our planet! As Errol White said: "We still do not know the mechanics of evolution in spite of the overconfident claims in some quarters, nor are we likely to make further progress in this by the classical methods of pale-

---

40. Gould, Stephen Jay and Niles Eldredge, "Punctuated Equilibria: The Tempo and Mode of Evolution Reconsidered," *Paleobiology,* 3 (2), 1977, p. 115.
41. Carroll, Robert L., *Patterns and Processes of Vertebrate Evolution,* p. 146.
42. Gould and Eldredge, *Paleobiology,* vol. 3, 1977, p. 147.

ontology or biology; and we shall certainly not advance matters by jumping up and down shrilling, 'Darwin is god and I, So-and-so, am his prophet.'"[43]

Fossils are the remains of living creatures, both plants and animals, or their tracks. These are found in sedimentary rock. Sedimentary rock is composed of strata, which are layers of stone piled up like a layer cake. (Strata is the plural of stratum.) Sedimentary rock is fossil-bearing or fossiliferous rock. Fossil hunters use the word *taxa* (*taxon* is the singular) to describe the basic, different types of plants and animals found in the fossil record. By this they generally mean species, although sometimes they mean *genera* or more composite classifications, such as *families* or even *phyla.* Taxa is thus something of a loose term. *Higher taxa* would mean the larger creatures, such as vertebrates (animals with backbones).

"The part of geology that deals with the tracing of the geologic record of the past is called *historic geology.* Historic geology relies chiefly on *paleontology,* the study of fossil evolution, as preserved in the fossil record, to identify and correlate the lithic records of ancient time" (O. D. von Engeln and K. E. Caster, *Geology* [1952], p. 423).

These fossil remains may be shells, teeth, bones, or entire skeletons. A fossil may also be a footprint, a bird track, or the tail marks of a passing lizard. It can even include rain drops. Many fossils no longer contain their original material, but are composed of mineral deposits that have infiltrated them and taken on their shapes. Fossils are extremely important to evolutionary theory, for they provide our only record of plants and animals in ancient times. The fossil record is of the highest importance as an icon for evolution. In these fossils, scientists should be able to find all the evidence needed to prove that one species has evolved out of another.

"Although the comparative study of living animals and plants may give very convincing circumstantial evidence, fossils provide the only historical documentary evidence that life has evolved from simpler to more complex forms."[44]

---

43. White, Errol, *Proceedings of the Linnean Society,* London, 177:8 (1966).
44. Dunbar, Carl O., *Historical Geology* (1949), p. 52.

"Fortunately there is a science which is able to observe the progress of evolution through the history of our Earth. Geology traces the rocky strata of our Earth, deposited one upon another in the past geological epochs through hundreds of millions of years, and finds out their order and timing and reveals organisms which lived in all these periods. Paleontology, which studies the fossil remains, is thus enabled to present organic evolution as a visible fact."[45]

The studies of fossils and mutations are the two key evidences of evolution. The fossil evidence proves or disproves whether evolution has occurred in the past and mutational facts prove or disprove whether it can occur at all.

Eldredge and Tattersall make an important comment:

> That individual kinds of fossils remain recognizably the same throughout the length of their occurrence in the fossil record had been known to paleontologists long before Darwin published his Origin. Darwin himself . . . prophesied that future generations of paleontologists would fill in these gaps by diligent search. . . . One hundred and twenty years of paleontological research later, *it has become abundantly clear that the fossil record will not confirm this part of Darwin's predictions.* Nor is the problem a miserably poor record. The fossil record simply shows that this prediction is wrong. The observation that species are amazingly conservative and static entities throughout long periods of time has all the qualities of *the emperor's new clothes: everyone knew it but preferred to ignore it. Paleontologists*, faced with a recalcitrant record obstinately refusing to yield Darwin's predicted pattern, *simply looked the other way.*[46]

Likewise, the American paleontologist Steven M. Stanley describes how the Darwinist doctrine, which dominates the world of science,

45. Goldschmidt, Richard B., "An Introduction to a Popularized Symposium on Evolution," *Scientific Monthly*, Vol. 77, October 1953, p. 184.
46. Eldredge, N., and I. Tattersall, *The Myths of Human Evolution*, Columbia University Press, 1982, pp. 45–46.

has ignored this reality demonstrated by the fossil record: "The known fossil record is not, and never has been, in accord with gradualism. What is remarkable is that, through a variety of historical circumstances, even the history of opposition has been obscured. . . . 'The majority of paleontologists felt their evidence simply contradicted Darwin's stress on minute, slow, and cumulative changes leading to species transformation' . . . *their story has been suppressed.*"[47]

This is probably why, of all scientists, paleontologists and geneticists are the most likely to publicly repudiate evolutionary theory in disgust (A. H. Clark, Richard Goldschmidt, Steven Gould, Steven Stanley, Colin Patterson, *et al*). They have spent their lives fruitlessly working, hands on, with one of the two main factors in the very center of evolution: the evidence (fossils) or the mechanism by which it occurs (mutations) and that part of the body within which it must occur (DNA).

Evolution depends on the fossils. Clearly because no evolution is occurring now, all that the evolutionists have to prove their theory is fossil evidence of life forms which lived in the past. If evolution is the cause of life on Earth, then there ought to be thousands of partly evolved fossil life forms. For evolution to occur, this had to occur in great abundance. The fossils should reveal large numbers of transmuted species—creatures which are half–fish/half–animal, and so forth.

UNIFORMITARIANISM

A basic postulate of evolution is the concept of uniformitarianism. According to this theory, the way everything is occurring today is the way it has always occurred on our planet. This point has strong bearing on the rock strata. Since no more than an inch or so of sediment is presently being laid down each year in most non–alluvial areas, then no more than this amount could have been deposited yearly in those places in the past. Since there are thick sections of rock containing

---

47. Stanley, S. M., *The New Evolutionary Timetable: Fossils, Genes, and the Origin of Species,* Basic Books Inc., N.Y., 1981, p. 71.

fossils, then those rocks and their contents must have required millions of years to be laid down. That is how the theory goes. The opposite viewpoint is known as catastrophism, and teaches that there has been a great catastrophe in the past—the flood—which within a few months laid down all the sedimentary rock strata entombing the animals contained within them which became fossils.

Naturalists, working in Paris a few years before Charles Lyell was born, discovered fossil-bearing rock strata. Lyell used this information in his important book, *Principles of Geology,* and divided the strata into three divisions. He dated one as youngest, another as older, and the third as very ancient. Lyell and others worked out those strata dates in the early nineteenth century, before very much was known about the rock strata and their fossils! Strata in England, Scotland, and France were the primary ones studied. Lyell based his age theory on the number of still-living species represented by fossils in each stratum. If a given stratum had few fossils represented by species alive today, then Lyell dated it as more ancient.

It has since been established that Lyell's theory does not agree with reality; the percentage of still-living species is very, very high throughout all the strata and varies from place to place for each stratum in different localities. Nevertheless, after quarreling over details, Lyell's followers extended his scheme and though they changed his initial major strata names, they held on to his mistake and elaborated on it. Although some of the strata names changed later in the nineteenth century, scientists in the twentieth century have been stuck with this relic of early nineteenth-century error. It is what they are taught in the colleges and universities.

THE ERAS

The fossil-bearing rock strata are said to fall into three major divisions, called *"eras."* At the top are the *Cenozoic era* rocks. Below them come the *Mesozoic era* levels. Next, is the *Paleozoic* stratum. At the bottom we find the *Cambrian,* which contains the lowest fossil-bearing rocks. Beneath that is the *Precambrian.* (*Cenozoic* means "recent life," *Mesozoic* means "middle life," and *Paleozoic* means "ancient life.")

This fossil/strata theory is genuinely archaic. The basics of the theory were devised when very little was known about strata or fossils. But geology and paleontology have been saddled with it ever since. Here are the dates when the various geological time scales were first developed:

The Periods
» Quaternary—1829
» Tertiary—1759
» Cretaceous—1822
» Jurassic—1795
» Triassic—1834
» Permian—1841
» Carboniferous—1822
» Devonian—1837
» Silurian—1835
» Ordovician—1879
» Cambrian—1835

The Eras
» Cenozoic—1841
» Mesozoic—1841
» Paleozoic—1838

Perhaps the most ridiculous part of this is that radio–dating of rocks, a process which did not exist when the nineteenth century theories were devised, is forced to fit those nineteenth century strata dates! It is done by using only a few test samples which fit the nineteenth century dates. The rest are discarded.

SEVEN EPOCHS OF THE CENOZOIC ERA
» Paleocene—65 million years ago
» Eocene—55 million years ago
» Oligocene—40 million years ago
» Miocene—25 million years ago

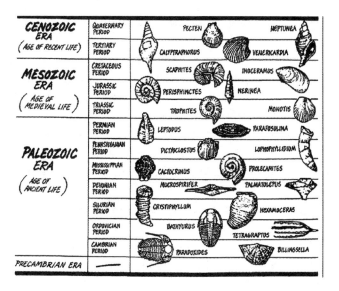

» Pliocene—10 million years ago
» Pleistocene—2 million years ago
» Holocene—10,000 years ago to present

If evolution was a fact, we should find in present events and past records abundant evidence of one species changing into another species. But, throughout all past history and in present observations, no one has ever seen this happen. Prior to written history, we only have fossil evidence. Scientists all over the world have been collecting and studying fossils for over 100 years. Literally millions have been collected. In all their research, this is what they discovered: (1) There is no evidence of one species having changed into another one. (2) Our modern species are what we find there, plus some extinct ones. (3) There are no transitional or halfway forms between species. Yes, there are *extinct* creatures among the fossils. These are plants and animals which no longer live on the Earth. But even scientists agree that extinct species would not be an evidence of evolution. Yet evolutionists parade dinosaur bones as a grand proof of evolution—when they are no proof at all! Extinction is not evolution!

So why are complex life forms found at the bottom of the strata? As we already mentioned, the lowest strata level is called the *Cam-*

brian. Below this lowest of the fossil–bearing strata lies the *Precambrian.*

The Cambrian has invertebrate (non–backbone) animals, such as trilobites and brachiopods. These are both very complex little animals. In addition, many of our modern animals and plants are in that lowest level, just above the Precambrian. How could such complex, multi–celled creatures be there in the bottom of the Cambrian strata? Suddenly, in the very lowest fossil stratum, we find complex plants and animals—and lots of them, with no evidence that they evolved from anything lower.

"It remains true, as every paleontologist knows, that most new species, genera and families, and that nearly all categories above the level of families, appear in the [fossil] record suddenly and are not led up to by known, gradual, completely continuous transitional sequences."[48]

Paleontologists call this immense problem *"the Cambrian explosion,"* because vast numbers of complex creatures suddenly appear in the fossil strata—with no evidence that they evolved from any less complicated creatures! What caused this sudden, massive appearance of life forms? What caused the strata? Why are all those fossils in the strata? What is the solution to all this?

The answer is that a great flood—the one described in the Bible in Genesis 6–9—rapidly covered the Earth with water. When it did, sediments of pebbles, gravel, clay, and sand were laid down in successive strata, covering animal and plant life. Under great pressure, these sediments turned into what we today call *"sedimentary rock."* (Clay became *shale;* sand turned into *sandstone;* mixtures of gravel, clay, and sand formed *conglomerate* rock.) All that mass of water–laid material successively covered millions of living creatures. The result is fossils, which today are only found in the sedimentary rock strata.

When the flood overwhelmed the world, the first to be covered were slow–moving animals, the next to be covered were somewhat larger, somewhat faster–moving animals, and so it went. Today we

---

48. Simpson, George G., *The Major Features of Evolution,* p. 360.

can dig into these rock strata and find that the lowest stratum tends to have the slowest-moving creatures; above them are faster ones. Evolutionist scientists declare these lowest strata are many millions of years old (570 million for the oldest, the *Cambrian),* and the topmost to be the most recent (the *Pliocene* at 10 million, and the *Pleistocene* at 2 million years). But, in actuality, we will discover that evidence indicates that all the sedimentary strata with their hoards of fossils were laid down within a very short time.

It is vital that we know whether there is enough evidence available to decide the fossil problem. Can we at the present time really know for sure whether or not, according to the fossil record, evolution has or has not occurred? Yes, we can know! Men have worked earnestly, since the beginning of the nineteenth century, to find evidences of evolution in the fossil strata.

"The adequacy of the fossil record for conclusive evidence is supported by the observation that 79.1 percent of the living families of terrestrial vertebrates have been found as fossils (87.7 percent if birds are included)."[49]

Luther Sunderland, author of *Darwin's Enigma* states:

Geology and paleontology held great expectations for Charles Darwin, although in 1859 [when he published his book, *The Origin of Species*] he admitted that they [already] presented the strongest single evidence against his theory. Fossils were a perplexing puzzlement to him because they did not reveal any evidence of a gradual and continuous evolution of life from a common ancestor, proof which he needed to support his theory. Although fossils were an enigma to Darwin, he ignored the problem and found comfort in the faith that future explorations would reverse the situation and ultimately prove his theory correct.

He stated in his book, *The Origin of Species,* "The geological record is extremely imperfect and this fact will to a large extent explain why we do not find intermediate varieties, connecting to-

49. Brown, R. H., "The Great Twentieth-Century Myth," *Origins,* January 1986, p. 40.

gether all the extinct and existing forms of life by the finest graduated steps. He who rejects these views, on the nature of the geological record, will rightly reject my whole theory" [quoting from
the sixth (1901) edition of Darwin's book, pages 341–342].

Now, after over 120 years of the most extensive and painstak-
ing geological exploration of every continent and ocean bottom,
the picture is infinitely more vivid and complete than it was in
1859. Formations have been discovered containing hundreds of
billions of fossils *and our museums now are filled with over 100 million fossils of 250,000 different species.* The availability of this profusion of hard scientific data should permit objective investigators
to determine if Darwin was on the right track."[50]

There are 100 million fossils housed in museums and other collections. That ought to be enough to locate the missing links and prove
evolutionary theory. Yes, enough information is now available that
we can have certainty, from the fossil record, about whether evolution ever did occur in our world! The following will provide you with
a brief summary of those facts.

"The reason for abrupt appearances and gaps can no longer be
attributed to the imperfection of the fossil record as it was by Darwin when paleontology was a young science. *With over 200,000,000
catalogued specimens of about 250,000 fossil species,* many evolutionary paleontologists such as Stanley argue that the fossil record
is sufficient."[51]

"In part, the role of paleontology in evolutionary research has
been defined narrowly because of a false belief, tracing back to Darwin and his early followers, that the fossil record is woefully incomplete. Actually, the record is of sufficiently high quality to allow us to
undertake certain kinds of analysis meaningfully at the level of the
species."[52]

"Over 10,000 fossil species of insects have been identified, over

50. Sunderland, Luther D., *Darwin's Enigma* (1988), p. 9.
51. Bird, W. R., *The Origin of Species Revisited* (1954), p. 48.
52. Stanley, S., *Macroevolution*, p. 1 (1979).

30,000 species of spiders, and similar numbers for many sea–living creatures. Yet so far the evidence for step–by–step changes leading to major evolutionary transitions looks extremely thin. The supposed transition from wingless to winged insects still has to be found, as has the transition between the two main types of winged insects, the paleoptera (mayflies, dragonflies) and the neoptera (ordinary flies, beetles, ants, bees)" (Hoyle, 1983, p. 43).

In spite of such an immense amount of fossil evidence, Heribert-Nilsson of Lund University in Sweden, after 40 years of study in paleontology and botany, said the missing links will never be found. "It is not even possible to make a caricature [hazy sketch] of an evolution out of paleobiological facts. The fossil material is now so complete that the lack of transitional series cannot be explained as due to the scarcity of the material. The deficiencies are real; they will never be filled."[53]

More than a century ago, enough evidence had been gathered from the study of fossils that it was *already clear* that the fossil gaps between Genesis kinds were unfillable. Even Charles Darwin admitted the problem in his book. ". . . Intermediate links? Geology assuredly does not reveal any such finely graduated organic change, and this is perhaps the most obvious and serious objection which can be urged against the theory [of evolution]."[54]

For over a century, hundreds of men have dedicated their lives, in an attempt to find those missing links. If the transitional forms, connecting one species with another, are really there—they should have been found by now. Sunderland, quoted above, said "Our museums now are filled with over 100 million fossils of 250,000 different species." Here, in two brief paragraphs, is a clear description of the enormity of this missing link problem:

"The time required for one of these invertebrates to evolve into the vertebrates, or fishes, has been estimated at about 100 million

---

53. Heribert–Nilsson, N., *Synthetische Artbildung (The Synthetic Origin of Species)*, 1953, p. 1212.

54. Darwin, Charles, *The Origin of Species,* quoted in David Raup, "Conflicts between Darwin and Paleontology," *Field Museum Bulletin,* January 1979.

years, and it is believed that the evolution of the fish into an amphibian required about 30 million years. The essence of the new Darwinian view is the slow gradual evolution of one plant or animal into another by the gradual accumulation of micro-mutations through natural selection of favored variants."

Dr. Duane Gish said:

If this view of evolution is true, the fossil record should produce an enormous number of transitional forms. Natural history museums should be overflowing with undoubted intermediate forms. About 250,000 fossil species have been collected and classified. These fossils have been collected at random from rocks that are supposed to represent all of the geological periods of earth's history. Applying evolution theory and the laws of probability, most of these 250,000 species should represent transitional forms. Thus, if evolution is true, there should be no doubt, question, or debate as to the fact of evolution.[55]

The above quotation provides an excellent summary of the fossil gap problem. **The fossil record purportedly contains a record of all the billions of years of life on Earth. If it takes "100 million years" for an invertebrate to evolve through transitional forms into a fish, the fossil strata should show vast numbers of the in-between forms. But it never does. Scientists discuss these facts among themselves; they have a responsibility to tell them to the public. The evidence supports the information given in the book of Genesis.**

---

55. Gish, Duane T., "The Origin of Mammals," *Creation: the Cutting Edge* (1982), p. 76.

CHAPTER 8

DATING THE STRATA AND FOSSILS

How are rocks dated? There are only two primary methods of long–ages dating: (1) *fossil–bearing rock strata*, (2) *radioactive dating*, plus carbon–14 dating.

There are vast quantities of fossils, scattered in various sedimentary strata throughout the world. Yet how are the rocks and the fossils dated? The rocks are dated from theories about the fossils and the fossils are dated from theories about the rocks. Let's examine this dating process more closely.

Man's *recorded history* only goes back about 4,500 years. The First Dynasty in Egypt has left us records that date back to about 2200 B.C. (That is the corrected date as determined by scholars; Manetho's account reaches to 3500 B.C.). Moses began writing part of the Bible about 1480 B.C. He wrote of events going back to about 4000 B.C.

Yet evolutionists claim that they can date this or that rock—going back into the millions of years. The entire geologic column—from bottom to top—is supposed to have taken two billion years, with millions of years being assigned to each level of strata. On what basis do they presume to think they can assign such ancient dates to the origin of various rocks? With the exception of some recently erupted volcanic lava, no one was present when any rocks were laid down. A man picks up a piece of rock from the distant past and, although he himself may be only half a century old, he claims to be able to date that rock as being 110 billion years old.

Rocks are not dated by their appearance, for rocks of all types (limestone, shale, etc.) may be found in all evolutionary "ages." Rocks are not dated by their mineral, metallic, or petroleum content, for any type of mineral may be found in practically any age. Rocks are not dated by the rocks they are near. The rocks above them in one sedimentary sequence may be the rocks below them in the next. The "oldest rocks" may lie above so-called "younger rocks." Rocks are not dated by their structure, breaks, faults, or folds. None of this has any bearing on the dating that evolutionists apply to rocks. Textbooks, magazines, and museum displays give the impression that it is the location of the strata that decides the dating, but this is not true.

Rocks are not dated by their height or depth in the strata, or which rocks are "at the top," "at the bottom," or "in the middle." Their vertical placement and sequence has little bearing on the matter. This would have to be so, since the arrangement of the strata shows little hint of uniformity anywhere in the world. The rock strata are not dated by the radioactive minerals within them. The dating was all worked out decades before anyone heard or thought of radioactive dating. There are so many ways in which radiometric dating can be incorrect one should not rely on uranium and similar minerals as reliable dating methods. The fact is that rocks are not dated by any physical characteristic at all. What then are they dated by?

The strata are said to be dated by fossils. Well, now we have arrived at something concrete. The strata are all mixed up, piled on top, under where they should go, or totally missing. But at least we can date them by all the fossils in them. But wait a minute! We cannot even use 99 percent of the fossils to date them by, since we can find the same type of fossils in one stratum as in many of the others. And in each stratum are millions of fossils, representing hundreds and even thousands of different species of plant and/or animal life. The result is a bewildering maze of mixed-up or missing strata, each with fossil prints from a wide variety of ancient plants and animals that we can find in still other rock strata.

Yet, amid all this confusion, evolutionists tell us that fossil dating is of extreme importance. That is very true, for without it the evolutionist scientist would have no way to try to theorize "earlier ages" on the Earth. Fossil dating is crucial to their entire theoretical house of cards. But if rocks cannot be dated by most of the fossils they contain, how are the rocks dated?

The strata are dated by what the evolutionists call *index fossils*. In each stratum there are a few fossils which are not observed quite as often in the other strata. As a pretext, these are the fossils which are used to "date" that stratum and all the other fossils within it. It may sound ridiculous, but that is the way it is done. What are these magical fossils that have the power to tell the men finding them the date—so many millions of years ago—when they lived? These special "index" fossils are generally small marine invertebrates—back-boneless sea animals that could not climb to higher ground when the flood came. Their presence in a sedimentary stratum is supposed to provide absolutely certain proof that the stratum is just so many millions of years younger or older than other strata. But then, just as oddly, the magic disappears when the index fossil is found alive.

"Most of the species of maidenhair are extinct; indeed they served as index fossils for their strata until one was found alive. The youngest fossil coelacanth is about 60 million years old. Since one was rediscovered off Madagascar, they are no longer claimed as 'index fossils'—fossils which tell you that all other fossils in that layer are the same ripe old age."[56]

In reality, within each stratum is to be found an utter confusion of thousands of different types of plants and/or animals. The evolutionists maintain that if just one of a certain type of creature (an index fossil) is found anywhere in that stratum, it must automatically be given a certain name, and more, a certain date millions of years ago when all the creatures in that stratum are supposed to have lived. Yet, just by examining that particular index fossil, there is no way to tell that it lived so many millions of years ago. It is all part of a marvelous theory, which is actually nothing more than a grand evolutionary hoax. Experienced scientists denounce it as untrue.

Any rock containing fossils of one type of trilobite *(Paradoxides)* is classified as Cambrian, thus dating all creatures in that rock to a

---

56. Pitman, Michael, *Adam and Evolution* (1984), pp. 186, 198.

period 600 million years in the past. But rocks containing another type of trilobite *(Bathyurus)* are classified as Ordovician, which is a period claimed to have spanned 45 million years and begun 480 million years ago. How can anyone come up with such ancient dates simply by examining two different varieties of trilobite? The truth is that it cannot be done. It is science fiction to even pretend to do so.

Added to this is the problem of mixed-up index fossils—when index fossils from different levels are found together. As we analyze one aspect after another of evolution (stellar, geologic, biologic, genetic, and so forth), we find it all to be little more than carefully contrived science fiction. But here comes the catch: How can evolutionist geologists know what dates to apply to those index fossils?

Darwinists theorize which animals came first and when they appeared on the scene. And then they date the rocks according to their theory. Not according to the wide mixture of fossil creatures in the rock, but by assigning dates based on their theory to certain index fossils. This is a colossal hoax.

The conclusions about which fossils came first are based on the assumptions of evolution. Rock strata are studied, a few index fossils are located (when they can be found at all), and each stratum is then given a name. Since the strata are above, below, and in–between one another and most of the strata are missing in any one location, just how can the theorists possibly date each stratum? They do it by applying evolutionary speculation to what they imagine those dates should be. This type of activity classifies as interesting fiction, but it should surely not be regarded as science. The truth is this: It was the evolutionary theory that was used to date the fossils, not the strata and not the index fossils. "Vertebrate paleontologists have relied upon 'stage of evolution' as the criterion for determining the chronologic relationships of faunas. Before establishment of physical dates, evolutionary progression was the best method for dating fossiliferous strata."[57]

---

57. Evernden, J. F., O. E. Savage, G. H. Curtis, and G. T. James, "K/A Dates and the Cenozoic Mammalian Chronology of North America," *American Journal of Science,* February 1964, p. 166.

"Fossiliferous strata" means fossil-bearing strata. Keep in mind that only sedimentary rocks have fossils, for they were the sediments laid down at the time of the flood, which hardened under pressure and dried into rock. You will find no fossils in granite, basalt, and so forth. The dating of each stratum—and all the fossils in it—is supposedly based on index fossils, when it is actually based on evolutionary speculations, and nothing more. The index fossils are dated by theory. Amid all the confusion of mixed up and missing strata, there would be no possible way to date rocks—or fossils—by the catastrophic conditions found in sedimentary strata. It is all utter confusion. So evolutionists apply a theory to the strata. Scientists decided that certain water worms in one stratum are 80,000 years older than certain water worms in another stratum. Then they date all the other fossils in those same strata accordingly. (That is a little foolish, is it not? How can you date a water worm to so many hundred million years ago?)

> Because of the sterility of its concepts, historical geology, which includes paleontology [the study of fossils] and stratigraphy [the study of rock strata], has become static and unreproductive. Current methods of delimiting intervals of time, which are the fundamental units of historical geology and of establishing chronology, are of dubious validity. Worse than that, the criteria of correlation—the attempt to equate in time, or synchronize, the geological history of one area with that of another—are logically vulnerable. The findings of historical geology are suspect because the principles upon which they are based are either inadequate, in which case they should be reformulated, or false, in which case they should be discarded. Most of us [geologists] refuse to discard or reformulate, and the result is the present deplorable state of our discipline.[58]

Big names and big numbers have been assigned to various strata,

---

58. Allen, Robin S., "Geological Correlation and Paleoecology," *Bulletin of the Geological Society of America,* January 1984, p. 2.

thus imparting an air of scientific authority to them. Common people, lacking expertise in the nomenclature of paleontology, when faced with these lists of big words, tend to give up. It all looks too awesome to be understood, much less challenged. But the big words and big numbers just cover over an empty theory which lacks substantial evidence to support it. When we examine it, we find that the strata–dating theory is based on "circular reasoning."

Circular reasoning is a method of false logic, by which *this is used to prove that, and that is used to prove this.* It is also called "reasoning in a circle." Over 100 years ago, it was described by the phrase *circulus in probando,* which is Latin for "a circle in a proof." Circular reasoning is the fundamental principle of evolutionary logic.

There are several types of circular reasoning found in support of evolutionary theory. One of these is the geological dating position that "fossils are dated by the type of stratum they are in while at the same time the stratum is dated by the fossils found in it." An alternative evolutionary statement is that "the fossils and rocks are interpreted by the theory of evolution, and the theory is proven by the interpretation given to the fossils and rocks."

Evolutionists use their theory of rock strata to date the fossils and then use their theory of fossils to date the rock strata. A number of scientists have commented on this problem of circularity.

Ronald R. West, professor of paleobiology at Kansas State University, wrote this: "Contrary to what most scientists write, the fossil record does not support the Darwinian theory of evolution, because it is this theory (there are several) which we use to interpret the fossil record. By doing so, we are guilty of circular reasoning if we then say the fossil record supports this theory."[59]

Niles Eldredge, head of the Paleontology Department at the American Museum of Natural History, in Chicago, made this comment: "And this poses something of a problem. If we date the rocks by their fossils, how can we then turn around and talk about pat-

---

59. West, Ronald R., "Paleontology and Uniformitarianism," *Compass,* May 1968, p. 216.

terns of evolutionary change through time in the fossil record?"[60]

The curator of zoological collections at Oxford University wrote this: "A circular argument arises: Interpret the fossil record in the terms of a particular theory of evolution, inspect the interpretation, and note that it confirms the theory. Well, it would, wouldn't it?"[61]

Circular reasoning is the basis, not only of the fossil theory, but of the whole theory of evolution. First, reasoning in a circle is the basis of the "evidence" that evolution has occurred in the past. (The fossils are dated by the theory of strata dating; the strata are then dated by the fossils). Second, reasoning in a circle is the basis of the mechanism by which evolution is supposed to have occurred at any time. (The survivors survive. The fittest survive because they are fittest—yet, according to that, all they do is survive, not evolve into something better.) By the use of circular reasoning, evolutionary theory attempts to separate itself from the laws of nature.

Limiting factors of chemical, biological, and physical laws forbid matter or living creatures from originating or evolving. Actually, the entire theory of evolution is based on a vast circularity of reasoning. Because they accept the theory, evolutionists accept all the foolish ideas which attempt to prove it.

> But the danger of circularity is still present. For most biologists the strongest reason for accepting the evolutionary hypothesis is their acceptance of some theory that entails it. There is another difficulty. The temporal ordering of biological events beyond the local section may critically involve paleontological correlation, which necessarily presupposes the non-repeatability of organic events in geologic history. There are various justifications for this assumption but for almost all contemporary paleontologists it rests upon the acceptance of the evolutionary hypothesis.[62]

60. Eldredge, Niles, *Time Frames: The Rethinking of Darwinian Evolution,* 1985, p. 52.
61. Kemp, Tom, "A Fresh Look at the Fossil Record," *New Scientist* 108, December 5, 1985, p. 66.
62. Kitts, David G., "Paleontology and Evolutionary Theory," *Evolution,* September 1974, p. 466.

As one studies the fossil record, they come upon a variety of serious problems which undermine the strata/fossil theory. Three of the most important are these: (1) At the very bottom of all the strata (the geologic column) is the *Cambrian* strata, which is filled with complex, multi-celled life. This is the "Cambrian explosion" of sudden life forms all at once. (2) There are no transitional species throughout the column. This problem is also called "fossil gaps" or "missing links." (3) Mixed-up and out-of-order strata are regularly found. By themselves or together, they destroy the evolutionary argument of the rock strata. But there are many more problems.

THE MIRACLE OF TIME

It is thought that time can somehow produce evolution, if there is enough time in which to do it. The evolutionists tells us that, given enough time, all the insurmountable obstacles to spontaneous generation will somehow vanish and life can suddenly appear, grow, and flourish. "It is no secret that evolutionists worship at the shrine of time. There is little difference between the evolutionist saying 'time did it' and the creationist saying 'God did it.' Time and chance is a two-headed deity. Much scientific effort has been expended in an attempt to show that eons of time are available for evolution."[63]

Just what is time? It is not some magical substance. It is merely a lot of past moments just like the present moment. Imagine yourself staring at a dirt pile or at some seawater, at a time when there was nothing alive in the world but yourself. Continue carefully watching the pile or puddle for a thousand years and more. Would life appear in that dirt or seawater? It would not happen. Millions of years beyond that would be the same. Nothing would be particularly different. Just piled sand or sloshing seawater, and that is all there would be to it.

You and I know it would not happen in a full year of watching; then why think it might happen in an million years? Since a living creature would have to come into existence all at once and suddenly, with everything in order evolutionarily to survive, it matters not how

---

63. Wysong, Randy, *The Creation-Evolution Controversy* (1976), p. 137.

many ages we pile onto the watching; nothing is going to happen.

To say that life originated in that seawater in some yesteryear "because the sand and seawater was there long enough" is just wishful thinking; nothing more. It surely is not scientific to imagine that perhaps it came true when no one was looking. There is no evidence that self–originating life or evolving life is happening now, has ever happened, or could ever happen.

G. Wald said in "The Origin of Life," in his book *Physics and Chemistry of Life,* "Does time perform miracles?" He then explains something that you and I will want to remember: If the probability of a certain event occurring is only 1/1000 (one chance in a thousand), and we have sufficient time to repeat the attempts many times, the probability that it could happen would continue to remain only one in a thousand. This is because probabilities have no memory. However, Wald goes farther. He explains that if the event is attempted often enough, the total probability of obtaining it would keep reducing. If it is tried a thousand times and does not even occur once, and then is tried thousands of more times and never occurs, the chance of it occurring keeps reducing. If it is tried a million times and still has not occurred, the possibility of it occurring has now been reduced to less than one chance in a million. The point here is that time never works in favor of an event that cannot happen.

Can time change rocks into raccoons, seawater into turkeys, or sand into fish? Can time invent human hormones, the telescopic eye of an eagle, or cause the moon to orbit the Earth? Can it increase complexity, and invent organisms? The truth is that the longer the time, the greater the decay, and the less possibility that evolution could occur.

Two of England's leading evolutionary scientists, Hoyle and Wickramasinghe, working independently of each other, came to a different conclusion than Bernal's. The chance of life appearing spontaneously from non–life in the universe is effectively zero (Hoyle & Wickramasinghe, 1981, p. 141).

One of these researchers is an agnostic and the other a Buddhist, yet both decided from their analyses that the origin of life demands the existence of God to have created it. They wrote:"Once we see, however, that the probability of life originating at random is so utterly minuscule as to make it absurd, it becomes sensible to think that the favorable properties of physics, on which life depends, are in every respect deliberate [i.e., produced by an intelligent mind].... It is, therefore, almost inevitable that our own measure of intelligence must reflect higher intelligences ... even to the limit of God" (Hoyle and Wickramasinghe, *et al,* p. 144).

The *London Daily Express* (August 14, 1981) put the conclusion of these two scientists into headlines: "Two skeptical scientists put their heads together and reach an amazing conclusion: There must be a God." Hoyle and Wickramasinghe concluded in their book that the probability of producing life anywhere in the universe from evolutionary processes was as reasonable as getting a fully operational Boeing 747 jumbo jet from a tornado going through a junkyard.

For nearly two centuries, evolutionists have known that, since there was no proof that evolution had occurred in the past and there was no evidence of it occurring today, they would need to postulate long ages as the means by which it somehow happened. Weisz, in his book *The Science of Biology* (p. 636), tells us that by the beginning of the eighteenth century, evolutionists "recognized that any concept of evolution demanded an earth of sufficiently great age, and they set out to estimate this age."

Darwinists claim that our planet is 6.5 billion years old. Long ages of time are desperately needed by evolutionary theorists, for, whenever confronted with the facts disproving the possibility of evolutionary processes, they can reply, "Well, given enough time, maybe it could occur." Ironically, even if the Earth were trillions upon trillions of years old, evolution still could not have taken place. Long ages of time cannot prove or produce evolution. Evolutionary processes across basic types of life forms are impossible both in the short and long run.

In 1862, Thompson said the Earth was *20 million* years old. Thirty-five years later, in 1897, he doubled it to *40 million.* Two years later, J. Joly said it was *90 million.* Rayleigh in 1921 said the Earth has been here for *1 billion* years. Eleven years later, W. O. Hotchkiss moved the figure up to *1.6 billion* (1,600,000,000). A. Holmes in 1947 declared it to be *3.35 billion* (3,350,000,000), and in 1956 raised it to *4.5 billion* (4,500,000,000). Presently, the age of the Earth stands at about 6.*5 billion years.* Pretty soon, someone will raise it again. "These [dates for the age of the Earth] have changed, doubling on average every 15 years, from about 4 million years in Lord Kelvin's day to 4500 million now."[64]

"Dr. A. E. J. Engel, Professor of the California Institute of Technology, comments that the age for the Earth accepted by most geologists rose from a value of about 50 million years in 1900 to about 5 billion years by 1960. He suggests facetiously that 'if we just relax and wait another decade, the Earth may not be 4.5 to 5 aeons (1 aeon = 1 billion years], as now suggested, but some 6 to 8 or even 10 aeons in age.' "[65]

Evolutionary scientists tell us that the past stretches into over a billion years of life on the Earth. Man, we are informed, has been here over a million years. That is the theory, yet the facts speak far differently. When we look at those facts, as available from ancient studies of all types, we find that recorded history goes back only several thousand years. Before that time, we have absolutely no verification for any supposed dating method of science. The earliest paintings of people only date back a few thousand years, and show them to be just like ourselves: intelligent, capable people. If human beings have been on this planet for over a million years as theorized by evolutionists, then we should have a large amount of structures and written records extending back at least half a million years.

Apart from recorded history, which goes back no farther than about 2200–3000 B.C., we have no way of verifying the supposed accuracy of theoretical dating methods. In fact, not even the dating methods confirm the dating methods. They all give different dates. With the very rare exception, they always disagree with one another.

---

64. Pitman, Michael, *Adam and Evolution,* p. 235.
65. Morris, H. M., W. W. Boardman, and R. F. Koontz, *Science and Creation* (1971), p. 74 (referring to A. E. J. Engel, "Time and the Earth," *American Scientist* 57, 4 (1969), p. 461).

HISTORICAL RECORDS

If mankind has been living and working on Planet Earth for millions of years, why do we find records of man dating back only to about 2000–3500 B.C.? And why do these records, when found, reveal the existence of highly–developed civilizations?

The writings, language, and cultures of ancient mankind started off fully developed and are not found to have begun until about 2000–3000 B.C.

EARLY EGYPTIAN RECORDS

The earliest historical books are those of the Egyptians and the Hebrews. The historical dates assigned to the beginnings of Egyptian and Sumerian history are based primarily on king–lists. The earliest are the Egyptian king–lists, dating from about the First Dynasty in Egypt, between 3200 and 3600 B.C. But the evidence indicates that these dates should be lowered. An Egyptologist writes: "We think that the First Dynasty [in Egypt] began not before 3400 and not much later than 3200 B.C. . . . A. Scharff, however, would bring the date down to about 3000 B.C.; and it must be admitted that his arguments are good, and that at any rate it is more probable that the date of the First Dynasty is later than 3400 B.C., rather than earlier. "[66]

The problem with First Dynasty dates is they are based on the king–lists of Manetho, an Egyptian priest who lived many centuries later, in 250 B.C. Manetho's writings have only been preserved in a few inaccurate quotations in other ancient writings. Barton of the University of Pennsylvania points out the problem here: "The number of years assigned to each [Egyptian] king, and consequently the length of time covered by the dynasties, differ in these two copies, so that, while the work of Manetho forms the backbone of our chronology, it gives us no absolutely reliable chronology."[67]

Confusion in regard to Egyptian dating has continued on down to the present time. "In the course of a single century's research, the

---

66. Hall, H. R., "Egypt: Archaeology," *Encyclopedia Britannica,* 1958 edition, Vol. 8, p. 37.

67. Barton, George A., *Archaeology and the Bible,* p. 11.

earliest date in Egyptian history—that of Egypt's unification under King Menes [first king of the first Egyptian dynasty]—has plummeted from 5876 to 2900 B.C., and not even the latter year has been established beyond doubt. Do we in fact, have any firm dates at all?"[68]

It is difficult to obtain exact clarity when examining ancient Egyptian texts. A number of Egyptologists think that Manetho's lists *dealt not with a single dynasty—but with two different ones that reigned simultaneously* in upper and lower Egypt. This would markedly reduce the Manetho dates.

Manetho's king–lists give us dates older than that of any other dating records anywhere in the world. But there are a number of scholars who believe that (a) the lists deal with two simultaneously–reigning sets of kings, (b) that they are not numerically accurate, and (c) that Manetho fabricated names, events, numbers, and history, as did many ancient Egyptian pharaohs and historians, in order to magnify the greatness of Egypt or certain rulers. For example, it is well–known among archaeologists and Egyptologists that ancient Egyptian records exaggerated victories, while never mentioning defeats. The Egyptians had a center–of–the–universe attitude about themselves, and they repeatedly colored or falsified historical reporting in order to make themselves look better than other nations around them.

In contrast, it is highly significant that well–authenticated Egyptian dates only go back to 1600 B.C. Experts, trying to unravel Egyptian dating problems, have come to that conclusion. "Frederick Johnson, coworker with Dr. Libby [in the development of and research with radiocarbon dating], cites the general correspondence [agreement] of radiocarbon dates to the known ages of various samples taken from tombs, temples, or palaces out of the historical past. Well authenticated dates are known only back as far as 1600 B.C. in Egyptian history, according to John G. Read (*Journal of Near Eastern Studies,* 29, No. 1, 1970). Thus, the meaning of dates by C14 prior to 1600 B.C. is still as yet controversial. "[69]

---

68. Lehmann, Johannes, *The Hittites* (1977), p. 204.
69. Morris, Boardman, and Koontz, *Science and Creation,* p. 85.

Because Egyptian dates are heavily relied on by cosmologists, chronologists, historians, and archaeologists for their theories, Egyptian dating has become very important in dating the ancient world, and thus is quite influential. This is because it purports to provide us with the earliest historical dates.

CIVILIZATIONS

The Sumerians were the first people with written records in the region of greater Babylonia. Their earliest dates present us with the same problems that we find with Egyptian dates.

"Historical records of any human civilization before 4000 B.C. are completely absent."[70] It is highly significant that no verified archaeological datings predate the period of about 3000 B.C. When larger dates are cited, they come from radiocarbon dating or from methods other than written human records.

Oddly enough, man has accomplished more in the last 6,000 years than he did in the previous million years. This would be true in light of the fact that we have not one shred of evidence that man did anything in that previous 1 million years. "In the last 6,000 years, man has advanced far more rapidly than he did in the million or more years of his prehistoric existence."[71] The developer of radiocarbon dating was astounded to learn that there are no records of mankind prior to 3000 B.C.

> The research in the development of the [radiocarbon] dating technique consisted of two stages—dating of samples from the historic and the prehistoric epochs, respectively. Arnold [a coworker] and I had our first shock when our advisors informed us that history extended back only for 5,000 years.... You read statements to the effect that such and such a society or archaeological site is 20,000 years old. We learned rather abruptly that these numbers, these ancient ages, are not known accurately; in fact, the earliest histori-

---

70. Enoch, H., *Evolution or Creation*, p. 137.
71. Eisman, Louise and Charles Tanzer, *Biology and Human Progress* (1958), p. 509.

cal date that has been established with any degree of certainty is about the time of the 1st Dynasty in Egypt.[72]

Prior to a certain point several thousand years ago, there was no trace of man having ever existed. After that point, civilization, writing, language, agriculture, domestication, and all the rest suddenly exploded into intense activity. "No more surprising fact has been discovered by recent excavation, than the suddenness with which civilization appeared in the world. This discovery is the very opposite to that anticipated. It was expected that the more ancient the period, the more primitive would excavators find it to be, until traces of civilization ceased altogether and aboriginal man appeared. Neither in Babylonia nor Egypt, the lands of the oldest known habitations of man, has this been the case."[73]

Dates going back to 3000 to 4000 B.C. are estimated as the longest possible dates. "The Egyptian king lists go back to the First Dynasty of Egypt, a little before 3000 B.C. Before that, there were no written records anywhere."[74]

In Genesis 8:4, we are told that near the end of the flood, the ark came to rest in the region of the Ararat Mountains. This area is located in the far eastern portion of modern Turkey, close to Iran and Iraq (ancient Persia and Babylonia). In Genesis 10, we find *the Table of Nations,* a list of races and where they went after the flood. William F. Allbright, considered the dean of American archaeologists, regarded this table as an astonishingly accurate document. The raising of crops, animal husbandry, metallurgy, and building of towns and cities—all of our earliest records, in every instance—go back to the Near East. The exception to this would be the notoriously inaccurate early carbon–14 dating assigned to objects recovered from various parts of the world.

The civilizations spring into view suddenly. The Great Pyramid of Khufu is constructed of more than 2 million enormous blocks of

72. Libby, Willard, *Science,* March 3, 1961, p. 624.
73. Wiseman, P. J., *New Discoveries in Babylonia about Genesis* (1949), p. 28.
74. Renfrew, Colin, *Before Civilization* (1983), p. 25.

limestone each weighing two and a half tons in a structure nearly 500 feet high and 570 feet square at the base. The burial chamber lies at the bottom of a shaft beneath the structure, and as in other pyramids there are additional passages and chambers. Completed about 2885 B.C. by 300,000 men working for twenty years (St. Paul's took 35 years to build), this was the largest structure ever erected by man, and even today it is only exceeded by the Grand Coulee Dam in the United States. Yet only a century before the Great Pyramid was built, no stone building existed anywhere in the world. Does this look like Evolution?[75]

---

75. Enoch, H., *Evolution or Creation* (1967), p. 131.

CHAPTER 9

No Transitional Fossil Forms

One of the most startling facts about sedimentary strata around the world is the vast quantities of fossils they contain. Without a worldwide flood, it would be impossible for such huge amounts of plants and animals to have been rapidly buried. And without rapid burial they could not have fossilized. Yes, there are immense numbers of rapidly buried fossils.

About one-seventh of the Earth's surface is tundra, frozen mud, containing the fossil remains of millions of mammoths and other large and small animals. There are vast amounts of dinosaur bones found in many places in the world.

Over 300 different kinds of dinosaurs have been excavated from one place in Utah. Vast fossil beds of plants exist. Today, we call them coal beds.

In Geiseltal, Germany, were found the remains of 6,000 vertebrates. Great masses of amphibians have been found in the Permian beds of Texas. In the Texas Hill Country, huge masses of fossil clams have been unearthed, yet never are living clams so tightly packed together as we find here. Examining them, we find clamshells that are closed. When a clam dies, its shell opens—unless before death it is quickly buried under the pressure of many feet of soil and pebbles.

In one area alone in South Africa, there are about 800 billion fossils of amphibians and reptiles in an area 200,000 square miles. Old Red Sandstone in England has billions upon billions of fish, spread over 10,000 square miles, with as many as 1,000 fish fossils in one square yard. Trilobites are among the smallest of the fossils. They are found at the bottom of the strata, in the Cambrian. And the Cambrian, with its trilobites—is also found 7,000 feet high in the mountains. Yet trilobites were small shallow–sea creatures. What flood of waters carried them up there?

Forty-three hundred years ago, a great catastrophe, the flood, overspread the world. Vast beds of sedimentary fossil–bearing strata cover about three–fourths of the Earth's surface, and are as much as 40,000–feet thick, sedimentary strata that are filled with fish fossils. Yet when a fish dies today it never fossilizes. It bloats, floats, and then is eaten by scavengers and other small creatures.

FACT:
MEN HAVE SEARCHED FOR FOSSILS SINCE THE BEGINNING OF THE NINETEENTH CENTURY, AND THE FACTS ARE NOW AVAILABLE: THERE IS NO EVIDENCE OF EVOLUTION IN THE FOSSIL RECORD.

Several years ago, two scientists tried to make some fossils. According to the school textbooks, it should not be hard to do.

Rainer Zangerl and Eugene S. Richardson, Jr., placed dead fish in wire cages and dropped them into several Louisiana lagoons and bayous. When the men returned six and a half days later, they found that bacteria and scavengers had consumed all the soft parts of the fish and had scattered the bones in the cages. Though the strata have lots of animals in them, when an animal dies today it never fossilizes. It rots if the buzzards do not find it first. Dead animals do not normally produce fossils.

There is an abundance of fossilized plant life in the strata; yet, when a weed, bush, or tree dies, it turns back to soil. It does not harden into a fossil. It requires some very special conditions to produce fossils. Those conditions occurred one time in history. The evidence is clear that it was a worldwide phenomenon and that it happened very, very quickly.

A striking fact about the fossils is that they were obviously all laid down at the same time—and very, very rapidly. Where are the bison today? Most were slain by buffalo hunters in the Plains states of America over 100 years ago. But where are their fossils? None are to be found. Millions of bison died, but there are no fossil remains. They rotted, were eaten by scavengers, decayed, and slowly returned back to the Earth.

The fact is that fossils never form at the present time; yet, in the sedimentary strata, we find literally billions of them. Examination of the strata bearing them reveals it was obviously laid down by a massive flood of water. The sheer immensity of these fossil graveyards is fantastic. And to think that it never happens today!

It would be impossible for vast numbers of plants and animals to be suddenly buried under normal circumstances. Yet we find that the fossil animals were buried so quickly that food can be seen in many of their stomachs. Even the delicate soft parts of their bodies are visible, so rapid had been the burial. Quick, high compression adds to the evidence for extremely rapid burial. All of the life forms were suddenly flattened out. Sharks have been found flattened to one–quarter–inch in thickness with the tail still upright, suggesting sudden catastrophic burial. It took rapid action to do that.

What happened? Some terrible catastrophe occurred that suddenly overwhelmed the Earth. Fossil seashells have been found in the highest mountains of the planet, including the highest range of them all, the Himalayas, which reaches in an arc across central Asia.

FISH SWALLOWING FISH

Princeton University scientists were working in Fossil Lake, Wyoming, when they found a fossil fish that was swallowing another fish. Because both fish had been pressed flat by the sudden burial, the paleontologists could see one fish inside the other with only the tail sticking out of the larger one's throat. It was a perch swallowing a herring. Obviously, this required a very sudden event to capture and kill a fish swallowing a fish. Nothing like this happens today.

In the Hall of Paleontology at Kansas State University there can be seen a 14–foot fish that has swallowed a 6–foot fish. The fish that was swallowed was not digested, and both had been suddenly entombed.

In what forms are the fossils? There are millions upon millions of fossils. You may wonder what those fossils are like. Here are the seven primary types of fossils:

1. Hard parts (the bones and shells) of some plants and animals were preserved.
2. Carbon alone was preserved. This is where our coal beds came from.
3. The original form is preserved only in *casts and molds.* The original material dissolved away and a cast of its shape was preserved. This would also require sudden burial.
4. Sometimes *petrifaction of wood* occurred. An excellent example of this would be the Petrified Forest in Arizona, where we find entire tree trunks that have turned to stone. After sudden burial, each cell in the wood was gradually replaced by minerals from an underground flow of water.
5. Fossil footprints.
6. Ripple marks and rain drop splashes—Ancient hail imprints (which are quite different from raindrops) have never been found. The weather must have been consistently warm when the flood began (W. H. Twenhofel, *Principles of Sedimentation* [1950], p. 621).
7. Worm trails, droppings, feathers, and chemicals were preserved by sudden burial.

Another dramatic evidence of a catastrophic flood of massive proportions, the cause of the sedimentary strata, is the buried forests. Coal beds, of course, are one such example of buried forests.

One of the best places to see buried forests is *Specimen Ridge* in Yellowstone Park, in Montana. You will there find a succession of petrified tree layers. The uniformitarian evolutionists claim that the trees grew there, died, and were gradually covered by soil deposits as the dead trees continue to stand. After tens of thousands of years, additional trees died and were covered over by more millennia of soil deposits. But careful analysis of the entire ridge reveals a unity of age, burial conditions, and surrounding deposits. A succession of strong currents, interspersed with flows and volcanic showers from another direction, washed the sedimentary strata into place.

Stop and think of it a minute: Would a vertical tree die and stand there for half a million years while rock strata gradually covered it? Yet we find polystrate trees in the strata and even in coal beds.

Polystrate tree fossilized in the rock. Photos by Dr. Don Patton

The great majority of animals and plants that lived long ago were just like those alive today, with the exception of some extinct species. Here is a sampling of what you will find in the complete strata of the geologic column—but remember that this "complete" strata cannot be found in its entirety anywhere in the world. Beginning at the bottom, and proceeding to the top, this is what we find:

> Precambrian ....algae, bacteria, fungi
> Cambrian .... sponges, snails, jellyfish
> Ordovician.........clams, starfish, worms
> Silurian................. scorpions, corals
> Devonian .... sharks, lungfish
> Carboniferous..........ferns, cockroaches
> Permian ....beetles, dragonflies
> Triassic.....................pines, palms
> Jurassic............... crocodiles, turtles
> Cretaceous............... ducks, pelicans
> Paleocene............... rats, hedgehogs

Eocene. . . . . lemurs, rhinoceroses
Oligocene . . . . beavers, squirrels, ants
Miocene . . . . camels, birds
Pliocene . . . . horses, elephants
Pleistocene . . . . .man

It is obvious from the above list that the species we had before, we have now. Those fossils are just like their counterparts living today. Yes, there are some extinct species, for some kinds have died out. But it is of interest that a number of the anciently extinct species have in recent years been found to be still living.

Here are some of the thousands of creatures alive today that are totally identical to what they supposedly looked like millions of years ago:

» cockroach—250 million years
» starfish—500 million years
» shark—181 million years
» sea urchin—100 million years
» ginkgo tree—200 million years
» dragonfly—170 million years
» bacteria—600 million years

LIVING FOSSILS

There are species found only in rock strata, and supposedly millions of years old, which have been declared extinct for millions of years. This has been considered another proof of evolution, although extinction is no evidence of evolution; evolving into new life forms is.

In recent decades a number of these "extinct for millions of years" species have been found to not be extinct after all. The big question is this: Where, then, were they all those millions of years they were missing from the upper rock strata?

"There is, for example, the fact that some creatures fail to evolve yet continue on quite successfully as 'living fossils.' Bees preserved in amber from the Tertiary period are almost identical with living bees. And everyone has heard of the coelacanth, supposed to have been extinct since the beginning of the Cretaceous period. The plant world also offers living fossils, such as the gingko, with a leaf unlike that of any modern tree."[76]

So many of these living fossils have been found that scientists now have given it a name to the study: cryptozoology, the study of hidden animals. According to evolutionary theory, they were once alive, were hidden for millions of years, and continue living today. Here are some of these living fossils, all of which are alive today:

(1) **Coelacanth fish**—the crossopterygian fish—extinct since Cretaceous. It has not been found in the strata for the past 50 million years, yet is alive today.

(2) **Metasequoia**—the dawn redwood—extinct since Miocene; not in the strata for the past 60 million years, yet it is alive today.

(3) **Tuatara**—a beakheaded reptile—extinct since Cretaceous; not found in the strata for the past 135 million years, but today is alive.

(4) **Neopilina**—a segmented deep-sea mollusk— extinct since Devonian. Although missing from the strata for the past 500 million years, it is alive now.

(5) **Lingula**—a brachiopod shellfish—extinct since Ordovician; not in the strata for the past 500 million years, yet it is happily living today.

The now-famous *coelacanth* was a large fish known only from its fossil and allegedly extinct for 50 million years. Extinct, that is, until several specimens were found in the ocean. The first was found in a fisherman's net off the coast of Madagascar on December 25, 1938. Since then eight more specimens have been found alive.

It only requires a moment's thought to arrive at a startling fact: How could the coelacanth have become extinct 50 million years ago, and then be found now? In order to be declared extinct such a long time ago, the creature would obviously have had to have been found by paleontologists in older strata, and then not found at all in more

---

76. Taylor, G. R., *Great Evolution Mystery* (1983), pp. 25–26.

recent strata. Why is the coelacanth not in those more recent strata? Did it decide to hibernate for 50 million years?

This is clear–cut evidence that the sedimentary strata was the result of a rapid laying down of sediments during the flood, rather than the tortuously slow "100 years per inch" deposition pattern theorized by the evolutionists. Interestingly enough, some of these living fossils were formerly used by evolutionists as index fossils to prove the ancientness of certain rock strata. As you will recall, most index fossils are small marine organisms. They live so deep in the ocean that many of them (trilobites, graptolites, ammonites, and so forth) may still have representatives alive today, since we have but only slightly explored the ocean bottoms. There are scientists who believe they will find living trilobites before long. One living fossil, very close to the trilobite has already been discovered.[77]

Many other examples could be cited. Here are two:

In the nineteenth century, hunters reported tales among Congo tribesmen of a large, cloven–hoofed animal with a giraffe–like head and zebra stripes on its hindquarters and legs. Most zoologists dismissed it as a local legend, but Sir Harry H. Johnston was fascinated when he read about this unknown beast of the deep forest. Years later, he launched an expedition in search of the creature, which the natives called *okapi*. "After a nearly disastrous series of misadventures, he finally captured an okapi in 1906. One of the few large mammals discovered in the twentieth century, the okapi turned out to be a living representative of a genus *(Palaeofragus)* known from fossils and believed by zoologists to have been extinct for 30 million years" (Milner, 1990, p. 102).

According to *Science News* (June 9, 1990, p. 359), a species of dogwood tree, the *Diplopanax stachyanthus,* was believed by botanists to have died out about 4 million years ago. Apparently only fossil records remained of this tree.

But now a botanist at Washington State University has examined the fossil fruit of trees believed to be 15 million years old and

---

77. "Living Fossil Resembles Long-extinct Trilobite," *Science Digest,* December 1957.

found them to be essentially identical to the fruit of a dogwood family discovered in China in 1928.

"But wait a minute. If evolution is driven by the survival of the fittest, then I would expect older and inferior species to die out and be replaced by newer and better evolved species. If that is the case, what is around today? It should have died out long ago. Or else the figure of 15 million years is grossly wrong. In either case, something is evidently wrong with the theory of evolution."[78]

The existence of "living fossils" is a serious one for the evolutionist. Evolutionary theory is based on several concepts, two of which are violated here: (1) If a species becomes extinct, it cannot come back to life. (2) Species evolve upward, and can never return back to an earlier form. If that particular species has not existed for the past 15 million years, how then can it exist today?

78. Vun Kannon, Bob, "A Living Fossil," *The Adventure,* September 1990.

CHAPTER 10

PROBLEMS WITH THE GEOLOGIC STRATA

The sedimentary rock strata are frequently not arranged as they ought to be if they had been quietly laid down over millions of years. Five primary problems are (1) fossils in wrong places, (2) missing strata, (3) geosynclines, (4) megabreccias, and (5) over-thrusts.

The strata charts in the textbooks and popular magazines look so very complete and organized. Yet, in truth, this is not so. The problems are so serious that running controversies were carried on for years between feuding strata experts. Because the evidence was so confused, no one knew who was right. Finally, they arbitrarily settled on the patterns that are on the strata charts we use today.

For example, there is the *Sedgwick–Murchison–la Beche controversy*, which was fought over the Cambrian, Silurian, and Devonian strata systems.

Sedgwick was the first to describe the fossils of the lower Graywacke strata, which he named the Cambrian system after an ancient name for Wales. Eventually, studies led them to different levels of the Graywacke, where the mercurial and territorial Murchison claimed much of Sedgwick's domain for his newly founded Silurian system.

"Inevitably, almost all of the members of the Geological Society were drawn into the fray, and, when another geologist of the time, Sir Henry Thomas de la Boche, claimed part of the Graywacke for his

Devonian period, the battle lines were drawn. For nearly a decade the Great Devonian Controversy, as it was called, raged on in the scientific journals. The political maneuvering behind the scenes was almost as convoluted as the Graywacke itself" (Milner, 1990, p. 401).

Elsewhere, Milner explains how Murchison solved the controversy: "The men were completely unable to agree on where the natural boundaries occurred. Murchison, however, found a way to resolve the dispute. He got himself appointed director of the National Geological Survey and simply ordered that the name 'Cambrian' be deleted from all government books and geological maps" (Milner, 1990, p. 69)

Later, after both men were dead, part of Murchison's Silurian was renamed Cambrian. Have you ever noticed that, on the standard strata time charts, certain fossils will always be in certain strata? That is another generalization in the evolutionary theory that does not prove to be correct. In reality, fossils are frequently found in the wrong place, especially far below the strata where they are first supposed to have evolved into existence.

There are three ways that the experts deal with this problem: (1) ignore the evidence; (2) when large numbers of fossils are found in solid rock below their proper strata, they are said to have been *downwashed* through the solid rock into lower strata; and (3) when they are found above their theoretical strata, they are said to have *reworked* themselves into a higher strata. That is, they slipped, slid, or fell up through solid rock into higher levels.

As noted, reworking and downwash are used to explain fossils which, by their location, disprove the theory. (Overthrusts are used to explain much larger numbers of such fossils.)

"Fossils frequently occur where they are not 'supposed' to. It is then claimed that either the fauna [animals] or flora [plants] have lived longer than previously known (simple extension of stratigraphic range) or that the fossil has been reworked. In *'reworking,'* it is claimed that the fossil has been eroded away from a much older host rock and has thus been incorporated into a rock of more recent age. The reciprocal situation is *'downwash,'* where it is claimed that an organism has been washed down into rock much older than the time it lived and has become fossilized."[79]

A related problem concerns the fact that pollen from flowering plants has been found in Cambrian and even on top of Precambrian rock. This, of course, is in total disagreement with evolutionary theory, which maintains that flowering plants did not exist until many millions of years later. This would mean that the Cambrian explosion included flowering plants.

Still another problem in the fossil record has been given the name skipping. A species will be in a stratum, and totally disappear from the next stratum or two above that, and then reappear again. As mentioned earlier, in some cases a species disappears, never again to be seen until our own time when—there it is—alive and well on planet Earth.

The problems with the geologic column of strata and fossils keep getting worse. We have been discussing problems with the fossils, but now we will turn our attention to the strata itself. We learn that here the situation becomes totally unmanageable. Evolutionary theory falls helpless in trying to reconcile these insoluble hurdles to its success. Surprising as it may seem, the only evidence for the geologic succession of life is found in the strata charts of the geologists and in their imagination.

Nowhere in geological formations can we find (1) all the strata in order; (2) all the strata—even out of order; or (3) most of the strata, in or out of order. Instead we only find little bits here and there, and frequently they are mixed up (out of their theoretical sequence).

Never are all the strata in the theoretical geologic column to be found in one complete sandwich anywhere in the world! Most of the time, there only two to eight of the 21 theoretical strata found. Even that classic example of rock strata, the Grand Canyon, only has about half of them. But the missing strata should be there. How can strata be missing? Yet this is the way it is everywhere on Earth. In the Southwest United States, in order to find *Paleozoic* strata, we would

79. Woodmorappe, John, "An Anthology of Matters Significant to Creationism and Diluviology: Report 2," *Creation Research Society Quarterly*, March 1982, p. 209.

need to go to the Grand Canyon. To find *Mesozoic* strata requires a trip to eastern Arizona. To find *Tertiary* strata, off we go to New Mexico. Nowhere is the entire geologic column of the evolutionists to be found, for it is an imaginary column.

"Practically nowhere on the earth can one find the so-called 'geologic column.' In fact, at most places on the continents, over half the 'geologic periods' are missing! Only 15–20 percent of the earth's land surface has even one–third of these periods in the correct consecutive order. Even within the Grand Canyon, over 150 million years of this imaginary column are missing. Using the assumed geologic column to date fossils and rocks is fallacious" (Brown, 1989, p. 15).

> Data from continents and ocean basins show that the ten [strata] systems are poorly represented on a global scale: approximately 77 percent of the earth's surface area on land and under the sea has *seven or more* (70 percent or more) of the strata system *missing* beneath; 94 percent of the earth's surface has *three or more* systems *missing* beneath; and an estimated 99.6 percent has *at least one missing* system. Only a few locations on earth (about 0.4 percent of its area) have been described with the succession of the ten systems beneath (west Nepal, west Bolivia, and central Poland). . . . The entire geologic column, composed of complete strata systems, exists only in the diagrams drawn by geologists!"[80]

Evolutionists explain that the proper word for these problems is *unconformities*; it would not do for scientists to use the phrase missing strata, for if they are missing, then where did they go? Did billions of years of life on Earth suddenly vanish?

How can it be that the geologic column is so incomplete, when evolutionary theory teaches that it was quietly, slowly laid down uniformly over millions of years? The truth is that the rock strata point us back to a terrible worldwide catastrophe—a flood—not to millions of years of gradual soil deposits from dead plants and wind-blown soil.

---

80. Austin, S. A., *Impact 137*, November 1984, p. 2 [emphasis his].

THE GRAND CANYON

A visitor to the Grand Canyon gazes down upon a major fissure in the Earth's surface that is a mile deep. At the bottom of this canyon, the Colorado River winds its way for 200 miles. By the time the visitor departs, his head spins with U.S. Park Service lectures, diagrams, and films about names such as *Kaibab, Toroweap, Devonian, Permian,* and *Cambrian,* and numbers ranging through millions of years. But what the tourists are not told is that the Grand Canyon—which has more strata than most areas—only has five of the twelve major strata systems. It has the first, fifth, sixth, and seventh strata, with small portions here and there of the fourth. Totally missing are the second, third, eighth, ninth, tenth, eleventh, and twelfth.

Listed below are the twelve major strata systems—from top to bottom—as they are given in the schoolbook charts of the so-called geologic column. The strata which are found in the Grand Canyon are shown in capital letters. The Devonian, which is only found in part here and there in Grand Canyon strata, is in italic:

12—Quaternary
11—Tertiary
10—Cretaceous
 9—Jurassic
 8—Triasssic
 7—PERMIAN
 6—PENNSYLVANIAN
 5—MISSISSIPPIAN
 4—*DEVONIAN*
 3—Silurian
 2—Ordovician
 1—CAMBRIAN

The Grand Canyon was formed rapidly.

> The plain fact of the great number of para–conformities found in the Canyon is strong evidence in favor of short–term deposition. If many millions of years separated these various strata, how do evolutionists explain the anomaly of a river [the Colorado] taking

"only a few million" years to cut through some 8,000 feet of sediments which supposedly took up to 500 million years to be laid down, when those same strata exhibit no sign of erosion themselves. The obvious and simplest explanation is that these sediments were laid down in too brief a time span to allow erosion, and then scoured out by a large body of moving water much bigger than the present–day Colorado, and not very long ago.[81]

All in all, the Grand Canyon is outstanding evidence of the Genesis flood. "One of the most spectacular evidences of what a year–long, worldwide flood would accomplish may be seen in the Grand Canyon of Arizona. This gigantic formation is in some places more than 5,000 feet deep, 25,000 feet across, and extends for more than 100 miles to the east and west."[82]

The Colorado River lies at the bottom of the Grand Canyon, yet it is a typical winding river—the type found in fairly flat terrain. Winding rivers do not cut deeply. It is the straighter, steeper rivers with swiftly rushing water which deeply erode soil and hurl loose rocks along its side downstream.

The Colorado is a serpentine river in flatter country. It could not possibly have carved out the Grand Canyon unless: (1) a colossal amount of water was flowing; (2) the sediments comprising the canyon walls through which it was cutting were soft; that is, they had only recently been laid down by flood waters and had not yet solidified into solid rock; and (3) a rather sudden event caused that flowage of water.

These are exactly the conditions which the flood would have provided. The Colorado River drained an immense area in Utah and eastern Nevada. A lake covered that entire area, and an uplift caused the water to rather suddenly drain out. Shortly after the flood, while volcanism was at its height and the strata were still soft, the ground heaved upward over a vast area, which emptied *Lake Bonneville.* That flowing water drained toward the southwest, forming the

81. Mehlert, A. W., *Creation Research Society Quarterly,* June 1987, p. 28.
82. Whitcomb, John C.,*World that Perished* (1988), pp. 74–75.

Grand Canyon. Great Salt Lake is all that remains of the ancient lake. If you ever visit the area, you will see the former shoreline of the lake, high on the surrounding mountains.

Notice that the Colorado did little in the way of hurling rocks downstream. This is because the Grand Canyon had not yet hardened into rock when the river cut through it. If the Colorado had carved the Grand Canyon out of solid rock, we would find huge tumbled boulders in and alongside the streambed. But this is not seen. In contrast, later glacial action after the rocks had hardened did move large boulders in other areas; for example, they are to be seen in the Merced River below Yosemite.

STRATA GAPS

There are not only fossil gaps; there are strata gaps as well. Together, they spell the doom of the evolutionary theory as it is applied to sedimentary strata and the fossil evidence.

The Earth is supposed to have gradually been covered by one after another of the twelve major strata systems listed above, over a period of millions of years. If that is true, why are a majority of those twelve strata systems missing from any given locality in the world? Why then are less than half present in that great classic of them all, the Grand Canyon? If the sedimentary rock strata were slowly formed over millions of years in an uniformitarian manner, then all the strata should be found throughout the world. Keep in mind that evolution teaches that each stratum represents the accumulated sediment from a span of millions of years at a certain earlier epoch in Earth's history. If this theory were true, then all the strata would have to be found evenly, everywhere on the globe.

Here is a statement in scientific jargon: "Many unconformity bounded units are considered to be chronostratigraphic units in spite of the fact that unconformity surfaces inevitably cut across isochronous horizons and hence cannot be true chronostratigraphic boundaries."[83]

---

83. Chang, C. Hong, "Unconformity–Bounded Stratigraphic Units," *Bulletin of the Geological Society of America,* November 1975, p. 1544.

Here, in everyday English, is the meaning of that statement: Many of the tilted, folded, and mixed-up fossil strata are theoretically supposed to measure long ages of time, but in reality there is such confusion that it is impossible for such strata to measure anything.

THE ROCKS REVEAL THE TRUTH

Now let's put the universal flood theory to the test. If it was the Genesis flood which suddenly formed the rock strata, then we would expect to find:

1. Pockets of inundated, covered animals here and there;
2. Mixed-up and missing strata everywhere we look;
3. Geosynclines (twisted and folded strata) found frequently;
4. Megabreccias (giant boulders) as a regular occurrence in the strata;
5. Upside-down strata;
6, Overthrusts, in which the so-called more recent strata lie buried deep beneath older strata;
7. Vertical tree trunks (polystrate trees) in place, from bottom to top spanning through various ages of strata;
8. The slowest marine creatures in the lowest strata, slowest land animals higher up;
9. Birds less frequently found since they could fly to the higher points;
10. Apes very difficult to find, and man almost impossible to find— since both would know how to reach the highest points and cling there. Their bodies would then float and decay without being covered by sediment.
11. Complex life forms would be found in rich profusion at the very bottom of the fossil-bearing rock strata (the Cambrian explosion), with next to nothing beneath it.
12. And, amid all the fossil strata, only the same separate, distinct species we now see on Earth and in the sea, plus some which have become extinct with no transitional forms to be found anywhere in the rock strata.

CHAPTER 11

COMPLEXITY AT THE BEGINNING

Because the waters of the flood first covered the creatures which were not able to rapidly escape to higher ground, some of the simplest animals are found in the lowest of the sedimentary strata. Yet those creatures have complicated internal structures. One of the most common creatures found in the lowest, or Cambrian, strata are the trilobites. These were small swimming creatures belonging to the same group as insects (arthropods). Yet careful study reveals that they had extremely complex eyes. The mathematics needed to work out the lens structure of these little creatures is so complicated that it was not developed until the middle of the last century. Here is how an expert describes it. Norman Macbeth, in a speech at Harvard University in 1983, said this:

> I have dealt with biologists over the last twenty years now. I have found that, in a way, they are hampered by having too much education. They have been steeped from their childhood in the Darwinian views, and, as a result, it has taken possession of their minds to such an extent that they are almost unable to see many facts that are not in harmony with Darwinism. These facts simply aren't there for them often, and other ones are sort of suppressed or distorted. I'll give you some examples.
>
> First, and perhaps most important, is the first appearance of fossils. This occurs at a time called the "Cambrian," 600 million

years ago by the fossil reckoning. The fossils appear at that time [in the Cambrian] in a pretty highly developed form. They don't start very low and evolve bit by bit over long periods of time. In the lowest fossil-bearing strata of all [the Cambrian], they are already there, and are pretty complicated in more-or-less modern form. One example of this is the little animal called the trilobite. There are a great many fossils of the trilobite right there at the beginning with no buildup to it [no evolution of life forms leading to it]. And, if you examine them closely, you will find that they are not simple animals. They are small, but they have an eye that has been discussed a great deal in recent years—an eye that is simply incredible. It is made up of dozens of little tubes which are all at slightly different angles so that it covers the entire field of vision, with a different tube pointing at each spot on the horizon. But these tubes are all more complicated than that, by far. They have a lens on them that is optically arranged in a very complicated way, and it is bound into another layer that has to be just exactly right for them to see anything. But the more complicated it is, the less likely it is simply to have grown up out of nothing. And this situation has troubled everybody from the beginning—to have everything at the very opening of the drama. The curtain goes up [life forms first appear in the Cambrian strata] and you have the players on the stage already, entirely in modern costumes.[84]

Remember, we are here discussing one of the most common creatures at the very bottom of the fossil strata. *Science News* declared that the trilobite had "the most sophisticated eye lenses ever produced by nature."[85] Each eye of the trilobite had two lenses! Here is what one of the world's leading trilobite researchers wrote:

In fact, this optical doublet is a device so typically associated with human invention that its discovery in trilobites comes as some-

---

84. Macbeth, Norman, speech at Harvard University, September 24, 1983, quoted in L. D. Sunderland, *Darwin's Enigma* (1988), p. 150.
85. *Science News 105,* February 2, 1974, p. 72.

thing of a shock. The realization that trilobites developed and used such devices half a billion years ago makes the shock even greater. And a final discovery—that the refracting interface between the two lense elements in a trilobite's eye was designed ["designed"] in accordance with optical constructions worked out by Descartes and Huygens in the mid–seventeenth century—borders on sheer science fiction. . . . The design of the trilobite's eye lens could well qualify for a patent disclosure."[86]

Extremely complicated creatures at the very beginning, with nothing leading up to them, that are the testimony of the strata. The rocks cry out and they have a message to tell us. Are we listening?

There are enormous numbers of complex trilobites in the Cambrian strata, yet below the Cambrian there is hardly anything that resembles a fossil. These little creatures not only had marvelously complicated eyes, they also had other very advanced features: (1) jointed legs and appendages, which indicate that they had a complex system of muscles; (2) chitinous exoskeleton (horny substance as their outer covering), which indicates that they grew by periodic *ecdysis*, a very complicated process of molting; (3) compound eyes and antennae, which indicate a complex nervous system; (4) special respiratory organs, which indicate a blood circulation system; and (5) complex mouth parts, which indicate specialized food requirements.

Another of the many types of creatures found in great numbers in the Cambrian strata is the segmented marine worm. As with trilobites, we find that they also had a complex musculature, specialized food habits and requirements, blood circulatory system, and advanced nervous system.

Evolutionists maintain that the fossil record goes from the simple to the complex. But researchers have discovered that the simple creatures were also complex. In fact, there are actually few examples in the fossil record of anything like the simple–to–complex progression. This is partly due to the fact that the fossils suddenly appear

---

86. Levi–Setti, Riccardo, *Trilobites,* 2nd ed., University of Chicago Press, 1993, pp. 54, 57.

A 530 Million-Year-Old Creation Miracle

THE TRILOBITE EYE

Trilobites, one of the oldest living species, appeared 530 million years ago. Their eyes represent the first visual system in the world. These eyes, with their extremely sophisticated and flawless design, deal a fatal blow to the claim of the theory of evolution that "Life evolved from primitive to advanced forms".

One of the living species that appeared suddenly in the Cambrian Period was an invertebrate sea-dwelling creature called the "trilobite". The eye of the trilobite had a "compound eye design". It consisted of hundreds of tiny eyes. Moreover, each of these tiny eyes had two different lenses. It is reckoned that this structure called the "doublet structure" allowed the trilobites to see underwater perfectly, without distortion. A professor of geology from the University of Harvard, David Raup says: The trilobites used an optimal design which would require a well trained and imaginative optical engineer to develop today. This perfect eye structure was brought into being 530 million years ago all of a sudden in its perfect form. No doubt, the sudden appearance of such a wondrous design can by no means explained by chance, all the more proving creation. Additionally, the compound eye system of the trilobites has survived to our day without a single change. Some insects such as bees and dragonflies have the same eye structure as did the trilobite. This situation disproves the evolutionary thesis that living beings developed from the primitive to the complex.

in great numbers and variety, too many for simple-to-complex progressions to be sorted out. Included here are complex organs, such as intestines, stomachs, bristles, and spines. Eyes and feelers show the presence of nervous systems. For example, consider the specialized sting cells *(nematocysts)* in the bodies of jellyfish, with their coiled, thread-like harpoons which are explosively triggered. How could this evolve?

The lowest stratum that has fossils is the Cambrian. Below that is the Precambrian, which has no fossils other than the occasional algae on its surface. Paleontologists call that amazing situation the "Cambrian explosion." Beginning with the very lowest of the fossil strata—the Cambrian—we find a wealth of fossil types. But each type (species) of fossil in the Cambrian is different from the others.

There is no blending between them. It requires evolving, blending across species, to produce evolution. But this never occurs today, and it never occurred earlier. Look at the fossils. In the ancient world there were only distinct species. Look at the world around you. In the modern world there are only distinct species.

When we look at the Precambrian stratum, the vast hosts of transitional species leading up to the complex Cambrian species are totally missing. Every major life group has been found in the Cambrian era. In the Cambrian we find sponges, corals, jellyfish, mollusks, trilobites, crustaceans, and, in fact, every one of the major invertebrate forms of life. In 1961, Kai Peterson wrote: "The invertebrate animal phyla are all represented in Cambrian deposits."[87] That means there, in the Cambrian fossil strata, is found at least one species from every phyla of backboneless animal. Only one phylum had been missing: the vertebrates (animals with backbones).

At the time when Peterson wrote, it was believed that no vertebrates appeared until the *Lower Ordovician* (just above the Cambrian). The oldest fish fossils, primitive *heterostracan* fish (class *Agnatha*) which were jawless, were from the Middle Ordovician Harding Sandstone of Colorado. But in 1977 that belief was shattered when fully developed vertebrate fish fossils (*heterostracan*) were discovered in the Upper Cambrian strata of Wyoming. Reported in *Science* magazine (May 5, 1978), this discovery placed every major animal phylum group in the Cambrian rocks. Although never discussed in school textbooks, this news came as a distinct shock to the professional world.

"[The 1976 discovery of *heterostracan* fish fossils in Cambrian is discussed in detail]. This discovery of fishes (vertebrates) in the Cambrian is without question the most significant fossil discovery in the period 1958–1979. The evidence is now complete that all of the major categories of animal and plant life are found in the Cambrian."[88]

For evolutionists, the situation continues to get worse. With the Cambrian explosion every major type of living thing appears suddenly. This fact totally devastates the basis of evolutionary theory. Although evolutionists prefer not to discuss it, the truth is that at least one representative of every phylum, plant and animal, has now been found in the Cambrian strata. Not only complex animal life, but complex plant life is represented in the Cambrian. Flowering plants are generally considered to be one of the most advanced forms of life

---

87. Peterson, Kai, *Prehistoric Life on Earth*, p. 56.
88. Lubenow, Marvin L., "Significant Fossil Discoveries Since 1958," *Creation Research Society Quarterly*, December 1980, p. 157.

in the plant kingdom. Spores from flowering plants have been found in Cambrian strata. Spores attributed to terrestrial plants have been found in Precambrian and Cambrian rocks in the Baltic. Whether some of these are from bryophytes is uncertain."[89]

During the Genesis flood, plants would tend to have washed into higher strata, but their pollen could easily have been carried into the earliest alluvial layers: the Cambrian and even the Precambrian.

> Just as fossils of most of the other land plants have been discovered in Cambrian deposits, so it is with the flowering plants. In 1947, Ghosh and Bose reported discovering angiosperm vessels with alternate pitting and libriform fibres of higher dicotyledons from the Salt Pseudomorph Beds and the Dandot overfold, Salt Range, Punjab, India. These are Cambrian deposits. They later confirmed that further investigation confirmed their original report, and the same results were obtained from the Cambrian Vindbyan System, and the Cambrian of Kashmir—these Kashmir beds also contained several types of trilobites. The review articles of Axelrod and Leclercq acknowledge these findings.[90]

No Life below the Cambrian

> Multi-cellular animals appear suddenly and in rich profusion in the Cambrian, and none are ever found beneath it in the *Precambrian.*[91]

The Cambrian rocks contain literally billions of the little trilobites, plus many, many other complex species. Yet below the Cambrian, in the Precambrian we find almost nothing in the way of life forms. The message of the rock strata is: suddenly, abundant life; below that, no life. And where this terrific explosion of abundance of life begins we find complexity, not simplicity of life forms.

---

89. Scagel, Robert F., *et al*, *Plant Diversity: an Evolutionary Approach* (1969), p. 25.

90. Lubenow, "Significant Fossil Discoveries Since 1958," p. 154

91. Cloud, Preston, "Pseudofossils: A Plea for Caution," *Geology,* November 1973, pp. 123–127.

It is true that in a very few disputed instances there have been found a few things in the Precambrian which some suggest to be life forms. But the majority of scientists recognize that, at best, these are only algae. *Blue-green algae* (although small plants) are biochemically quite complex, for they utilize an elaborate solar-to-chemical energy transformation (*photosynthesis*). Such organisms could have been growing on the ground when the waters of the flood first inundated it. The only macrofossils of widespread occurrence in the Precambrian are *stromatolites*. These are reef-like remnants thought to have been formed by microbial communities growing by photosynthesis (primarily blue-green algae) which precipitated mineral matter. So *stromatolites* are remnants of chemical formations, and were never alive.

The supposedly 3.8 billion-year-old *Isua outcrop* in Greenland was previously believed to contain the oldest evidence of life. Then in 1981 it was discovered that the evidence was nothing more than weathered crystals of calcium magnesium carbonates: "Further analysis of the world's oldest rocks has confirmed that microscopic inclusions are *not* the fossilized remains of living cells; instead they are crystals of dolomite-type carbonates, rusted by water that has seeped into the rock."[92]

Two years later, an update report in *New Scientist* on the world's oldest (Precambrian) rocks in Greenland said this: "Geologists have found no conclusive evidence of life in these Greenland rocks."[93] Scientists have remarked on the apparent sudden vast quantity of living creatures as soon as the Cambrian begins. All this favors the concept of creation and a Genesis flood, not that of slowly occurring evolution over millions of years.

THE GAP PROBLEM

First, there are no transitional species preceding or leading up to the

---

92. Henbest, Nigel, "'Oldest Cells' are Only Weathered Crystals," *New Scientist,* October 15, 1981, p. 164.
93. Peat, Chris, and Will Diver, "First Signs of Life on Earth," *New Scientist,* September 16, 1983, pp. 776–781.

first multi-celled creatures that appear in the Cambrian, the lowest stratum level. Second, there are no transitional species elsewhere in the fossil record. Third, the species that appear in the fossil record are frequently found in many different strata. Lastly, the great majority of the species found in the fossil record are alive today.

But of all these problems, the lack of transitional creatures (halfway between different species) is probably the biggest single crisis in the geologic column for the evolutionist. Indeed, it is one of the biggest of the many crises in evolutionary theory.

"Evolution requires intermediate forms between species, and paleontology does not provide them."[94] Throughout the fossils, we find no transitions from one kind of creature to another. Instead we find only individual, distinctive plant or animal kinds.

"It is a feature of the known fossil record that most taxa appear abruptly. They are not, as a rule, led up to by a sequence of almost imperceptible changing forerunners such as Darwin believed should be usual in evolution."[95] To make matters worse, in the fossil record we find the very same creatures that we have today, in addition to the few extinct types which died out before our time. Neither now nor earlier are there transitional forms.

"When we examine a series of fossils of any age we may pick out one and say with confidence, 'This is a crustacean'—or starfish, or a brachiopod, or annelid, or any other type of creature as the case may be."[96] In the rock strata, we find horses, tigers, fish, insects, but no transitional forms. For example, we find large and small horses, but nothing that is part horse and part something else. After giving years to a careful examination of the fossil record, comparing it with that of species alive today, a famous biologist on the staff of the Smithsonian Institute wrote these words:

All the major groups of animals have maintained the same relationship to each other from the very first [from the very lowest level of

94. Kitts, D. B., *Paleontology and Evolutionary Theory* (1974), p. 467.

95. Simpson, G. G., *The Evolution of Life,* p. 149.

96. Clark, A. H., *The New Evolution: Zoogenesis* (1930) p. 100.

the geologic column]. Crustaceans have always been crustaceans, echinoderms have always been echinoderms, and mollusks have always been mollusks. There is not the slightest evidence which supports any other viewpoint.

... From the tangible evidence that we now have been able to discover, we are forced to the conclusion that all the major groups of animals at the very first held just about the same relation to each other that they do today.[97]

This glaring fact is a repudiation of evolutionary theory. Evolutionists even have a name for the problem. They call it *fossil gaps.* A related problem is the fact that a great number of fossils span many strata, supposedly covering millions of years. This means that, throughout the fossil record, those species made no changes during those millions of years.

The links are missing. Nearly all the fossils are our present animals, and the links between them are just not there. Today, few scientists today still look for fossil links between the major vertebrate or invertebrate groups. They have given up! The links just do not exist and have never existed. Evolutionists know exactly what those transitional forms should look like, but they cannot find them in the fossil record. They are not to be found, even though thousands of men have searched for them since the beginning of the nineteenth century. Everywhere they turn, paleontologists find the same regular, distinct species that exist today, as well as some that are extinct. The extinct ones, however, are obviously not transitional forms. For example, the large dinosaurs are not transitional forms, but a definite species which became extinct in ancient times—probably by the waters of the flood.

The search to find the missing links and fill the gaps between the distinct kinds has resulted in enormous collections of fossils. Recall the earlier statements by Sunderland and Kier, that 100 million fossils have been examined by paleontologists around the world? ". . .

---

97. Ibid, pp. 114, 211.

The fossil record nevertheless continues to be composed mainly of gaps."[98]

FACT:

IF THERE ARE NO TRANSITIONAL FORMS IN THE FOSSIL RECORD, THERE HAS BEEN NO EVOLUTION.

The smaller, slower-moving creatures appear suddenly in the Cambrian. Above the Cambrian, the larger, faster creatures appear just as suddenly. And when these life forms do appear, they appear by the millions. Tigers, salmon, lions, pine trees, gophers, hawks, squirrels, horses, and on and on.

Evolution cannot explain this sudden emergence, and competent scientists acknowledge the fact:

"The abrupt appearance of higher taxa in the fossil record has been a perennial puzzle. Not only do characteristic and distinctive remains of phyla appear suddenly, without known ancestors, but several classes of a phylum, orders of a class, and so on, commonly appear at approximately the same time, without known intermediates."[99]

". . . It remains true, as every paleontologist knows, that most new species, genera, and families, and that nearly all categories about the level of families, appear in the record suddenly and are not led up to by known, gradual, completely continuous transitional sequences."[100]

An important principle noted by every paleontologist who works with fossils is known as *stasis.* Stasis means to retain a certain form, to remain unchanged; in other words, not to change from one species to another.

The problem for the evolutionists is the fact that the animals in the fossil record did not change. Each creature first appears in

---

98. George, T. Neville, "Fossils in Evolutionary Perspective," *Science Progress,* January 1960, pp. 1, 3.

99. Valentine, James W., and Cathryn A. Campbell, "Genetic Regulation and the Fossil Record," *American Scientist,* November–December, 1975.

100. Simpson, G. G., *The Major Features of Evolution* (1953), p. 360.

the record with a certain shape and structure. It then continues on unchanged for "millions of years"; and it is either identical to creatures existing now or becomes extinct and disappears. But all the time that it lived, there was no change in it; no evolution. There was no evidence of what paleontologists call *gradualism*, that is, gradual change from one species to another. There was only stasis. The gap problem (no transitional forms between species) and the stasis problem (species do not change) ruin evolutionary theories.

"The history of most fossil species includes two features particularly inconsistent with gradualism: *Stasis:* Most species exhibit no directional change during their tenure on Earth. They appear in the fossil record looking much the same as when they disappear; morphological change is usually limited and directionless. *Sudden appearance:* In any local area, a species does not arise gradually by the steady transformation of its ancestors; it appears all at once and 'fully formed.'"[101]

All of the fossils can be categorized into one of two groups: (1) plants and animals which became extinct, and (2) plants and animals which are the same as those living today. Neither category provides any evidence of evolution, for there are no transitional forms leading up to or away from any of them. All are only species. Some creatures became extinct at the time of the flood or shortly afterward. But all creatures which did not become extinct are essentially identical, both in fossil form and in their living counterparts today. This is a major point. No species evolution has occurred. The fossils provide no evidence of species evolution.

According to evolutionary theory, a massive number of species changes had to occur in ancient times, but we do not find evidence of this in the rocks. We should find large numbers of transitional species, but we don't. A leading paleontologist explains: "There are about 250,000 different species of fossil plants and animals known. In spite of this large quantity of information, it is but a tiny fraction of the diversity that [according to the theory] actually lived in the

101. Gould, Steven Jay, "Evolution's Eratic Pace," *Natural History,* May 1977, p. 14.

past. There are well over a million species living today and. . . [it is] possible to predict how many species *ought* to be in our fossil record. That number is at least 100 times the number we have found."[102]

FACT:
FOSSIL EVIDENCE DOES NOT HAVE ENOUGH DIFFERENT SPECIES AND REVEALS NO SUCCESSIVELY EVOLVING SPECIES IN ANCIENT TIMES

Fossil experts also admit that far too many "new species" names have been applied to fossils which have been found. Consider this:

It is known that scientists assign a different name to the same species if it is found in the rocks of a different period. Dr. Raup, head paleontologist at the Field Museum of Natural History in Chicago, says that as much as 70 percent of all the "new" fossil species found, are misnamed.

> Dr. Eldredge [American Museum of Natural History, New York City] was asked, "Do paleontologists name the same creatures differently when they are found in different geological periods?" He replied that this happens, but they are mistakes. When asked the same question, Dr. Patterson [British Museum, London] replied, "Oh, yes, that's very widely done." Next he was asked, "That doesn't seem quite honest. You wouldn't do that, would you?" He said that he hoped he wouldn't. Would not this practice make a lot more species? Dr. Raup [Chicago Museum] said it would; perhaps 70 percent of the species described [in the fossil rocks] are later found to be the same as existing species. So 70 percent of the new species named should not have been [given new names, but were], either through ignorance or because of the ground rules used by the taxonomists.[103]

102. Raup, David M., "Conflicts Between Darwin and Paleontology," *Field Museum of Natural History Bulletin,* January 1979, p. 22.
103. Sunderland, L. D., *Darwin's Enigma* (1988), p. 130.

Obviously, such a practice deepens the problem for the experts. "An assistant of Dr. Eldredge, who was studying trilobite fossils at the American Museum, explained to the author how he made the decision on naming a new species: 'I look at a fossil for about two weeks and then if I think it looks different enough, I give it a new name.' So it is simply a matter of judgment with no firm ground rules."[104]

The experts tell us there are millions of species when there are not. *Taxonomists* are the men who classify and give names to plants and animals. Among them, the *splitters* are the ones who find it easier to make up new names than go to the trouble of properly identifying a specimen in hand.

"We all know that many apparent evolutionary bursts are nothing more than brainstorms on the part of particular paleontologists. One splitter in a library can do far more than millions of years of genetic mutation."[105]

It is well-known among the experts that there are far more splitters out there than *lumpers*, simply because applying a new name for a fossil is easier and brings more fame than going through all the drudgery of researching who had named it earlier.

Edward Cope and Othniel Marsh were two major museum fossil collectors in the western U.S. They fiercely hated one another, and for decades consistently double-named specimens which had already been named earlier. "Sadly, in the later bitter rivalry between Cope and Marsh, Leidy [an earlier fossil collector] was all but forgotten. Paleontologist Henry Fairfield Osborn, director of the American Museum of Natural History, recalled that many of the Eocene and Oligocene animals had been given three names in the scientific literature: the original Leidy name and the Cope and Marsh names" (Milner, 1990, pp. 272–273)

It is an intriguing fact that if the fossil evidence supported any species modification it would be devolution, not evolution. Ancient

---

104. Ibid, p. 131

105. Ager, V., "The Nature of the Fossil Record," *Proceedings of the Geological Association,* Vol. 87, No. 2, 1976, p. 132 [Chairman of the Geology Department, Swansea University].

plants and animals were frequently much larger than any now living. Not only do we find no crossing over the species line among fossils, but we also discover that species are not evolving, but degenerating with the passing of time.

A cardinal principle of evolutionary theory is that creatures must evolve into more complexity as well as become bigger in size. But the fossil record bears out neither theory. There is clear evidence of the complexity to be found in invertebrates, the supposedly lowest form of life. But there is a size differential as well: "[Edward Drinker] Cope is known to many students only for 'Cope's Law,' which *asserts, roughly speaking, that everything goes on getting bigger. . . . Alas, it is not generally true. The modern tiger is smaller than the sabre-toothed tiger of the last ice age. . . . The horsetails of our ditches are tiny compared with the 60-foot horsetails of the Carboniferous. And where are the giant snails of the early Cambrian or the giant oysters of the Tertiary?"*[106]

---

106. Taylor, G. R., *Great Evolution Mystery* (1983), p 122.

CHAPTER 12

No Transitional
Human Forms

The Darwinist claim holds that modern man evolved from some kind of apelike creature. During this alleged evolutionary process, which is supposed to have started from 5 to 6 million years ago, it is claimed that there existed transitional forms between modern man and his ancestors. The theory of evolution is based on the hypothesis that the contemporary man of today has evolved from its primate (ape) ancestors.

According to this completely imaginary scenario, the following five basic categories are listed:

1. *australopithecines* (*Australopithecus*) or "South African ape"
2. *H. habilis* or "tool using man"
3. *H. erectus* or "upright walking man"
4. archaic *H. sapiens* or "old modern man"
5. *H. sapiens sapiens* or "modern man"

Evolutionists call the genus to which the alleged apelike ancestors of man belonged *Australopithecus*, which means "southern ape." *Australopithecus*, which is nothing but an old type of ape that has become extinct, is found in various forms. Some of them are larger and more strongly built (*robust*), while others are smaller and more delicate (*gracile*).

THE COLLAPSE OF THE FAMILY TREE

The next step in the imaginary human evolution is *Homo,* that is, the human series. These living beings are humans who are no different from modern men, yet who have some racial differences. Seeking to exaggerate these differences, evolutionists represent these people not as a "race" of modern man but as a different "species."

However, as we will soon see, the people in the *Homo* series are nothing but ordinary human racial types. According to the evolutionist claims, the living things in the *Homo* series are more developed than *Australopithecus,* and not very different from modern man.

The modern man of our day, that is, the species *H. sapiens,* is said to have formed at the latest stage of the evolution of this genus *Homo.* Fossils like "Java man," "Peking man," and "Lucy" appear in the media from time to time. They are included in one of the five groups listed above. Each of these groupings is also assumed to branch into species and subspecies, as the case may be. Some suggested transitional forms of the past, such as *Ramapithecus,* had to be excluded from the imaginary human family tree after it was realized that they were ordinary apes.[107]

---

107. Pilbeam, David, "Rearranging Our Family Tree," *Human Nature,* June 1978, p. 40.

By outlining the links in the chain as *"australopithecines > H. habilis > H. erectus > H. sapiens,"* the evolutionists imply that each of these types is the ancestor of the next. However, recent findings by paleoanthropologists have revealed that *australopithecines, H. habilis,* and *H. erectus* existed in different parts of the world at the same time. Moreover, some of those humans classified as *H. erectus* probably lived up until very modern times.

In an article titled "Latest *Homo erectus* of Java: Potential Contemporaneity with *Homo sapiens* in Southeast Asia," it was reported that *H. erectus* fossils found in Java had "mean ages of 27 ± 2 to 53.3 ± 4 thousand years ago" and this "raise[s] the possibility that *H. erectus* overlapped in time with anatomically modern humans (*H. sapiens*) in Southeast Asia"[108]

Furthermore, *H. sapiens neanderthalensis* (Neanderthal man) and *H. sapiens sapiens* (modern man) also clearly coexisted. This situation apparently indicates the invalidity of the claim that one is the ancestor of the other.

Intrinsically, all the findings and scientific research have revealed that the fossil record does not suggest an evolutionary process as evolutionists propose. The fossils which evolutionists claim are the ancestors of humans in fact belong to either different human races, or species of ape.

Then which fossils are human and which ones are apes? Is it ever possible for any one of them to be considered a transitional form?

In order to find the answers, let us have a closer look at each category. The scenario of human evolution is complete fiction. In order for such a family tree to represent the truth, a gradual evolution from ape to man must have taken place and a fossil record of this process should be able to be found. In fact, however, there is a huge gap be-

---

108. Swisher, C. C., III, W. J. Rink, S. C. Antón, H. P. Schwarcz, G. H. Curtis, A. Suprijo, Widiasmoro, "Latest *Homo erectus* of Java: Potential Contemporaneity with *Homo sapiens* in Southeast Asia," *Science,* Volume 274, Number 5294, Issue of 13 Dec 1996, pp. 1870–1874; also see, Jeffrey Kluger, "Not So Extinct After All: The Primitive *Homo Erectus* May Have Survived Long Enough To Coexist With Modern Humans," *Time,* December 23, 1996.

tween apes and humans. Skeletal structures, cranial capacities, and such criteria as walking upright or bent sharply forward distinguish humans from apes.

Another significant finding proving there can be no family–tree relationship among these different species is that species presented as ancestors of others in fact lived concurrently. If as evolutionists claim, *Australopithecus* changed into *H. habilis*, which, in turn, became *H. erectus*, the periods they lived in should necessarily have followed each other. However, there is no such chronological order to be seen in the fossil record.

According to evolutionist estimates, *Australopithecus* lived from 4 million up until 1 million years ago. The creatures classified as *H. habilis*, on the other hand, are thought to have lived until 1.7 to 1.9 million years ago. *H. rudolfensis*, which is said to have been more advanced than *H. habilis*, is known to be as old as 2.5 to 2.8 million years! That is to say, *H. rudolfensis* is nearly 1 million years older than *H. habilis*, of which it is alleged to have been the ancestor. On the other hand, the age of *H. erectus* goes as far back as 1.6 to 1.8 million years ago, which means that *H. erectus* appeared on the Earth in the same time frame as its so–called ancestor, *H. habilis*.

Alan Walker confirms this fact by stating that "there is evidence from East Africa for late–surviving small *Australopithecus* individuals that were contemporaneous first with *H. Habilis*, then with *H. erectus*."[109] Louis Leakey has found fossils of *Australopithecus, H. habilis,* and *H. erectus* almost next to each other in the Olduvai Gorge region of Tanzania, in the Bed II layer.[110]

There is definitely no such family tree. Stephen Jay Gould, the paleontologist from Harvard University, explains this deadlock faced by evolution although he is an evolutionist himself: "What has become of our ladder if there are three coexisting lineages of hominids (*A. africanus,* the robust *australopithecines,* and *H. habilis*), none

109. Leakey, R., A. Walker, "On the Status of *Australopithecus afarensis,*" *Science,* vol. 207, issue 4435, 7 March 1980, p. 1103.

110. Kelso, A. J., *Physical Antropology,* 1st ed., J. B. Lipincott Co., New York, 1970, p. 221; M. D. Leakey, *Olduvai Gorge,* vol. 3, Cambridge University Press, Cambridge, 1971, p. 272.

clearly derived from another? Moreover, none of the three display any evolutionary trends during their tenure on earth."[111]

When we move on from *H. erectus* to *H. sapiens*, we again see that there is no family tree to talk about. There is evidence showing that *H. erectus* and archaic *H. sapiens* continued living up to 27,000 years and even as recently as 10,000 years before our time. In the Kow Swamp in Australia, some 13,000–year-old *H. erectus* skulls have been found. On the island of Java, *H. erectus* remains were found that are 27,000 years old.[112]

One of the most surprising discoveries in this area was the 30,000–year-old *H. erectus,* Neanderthal, and *H. sapiens* fossils found in Java in 1996. The *New York Times* wrote in its cover story: "Until about a couple of decades ago, scientists conceived of the human lineage as a neat progression of one species to the next and generally thought it impossible that two species could have overlapped in place or time."[113]

This discovery reveals once again the invalidity of the evolutionary tree scenario regarding the origin of man. The concept that we are just animals, only slightly removed from apes, means that there are no moral standards, no laws worth obeying, no future, and no hope. The realization of this terrible truth even penetrated the gloom of Darwin's mind at times. "With me the horrid doubt always arises whether the convictions of man's mind, which has been developed from the minds of the lower animals, are of any value or at all trustworthy. Would anyone trust in the convictions of a monkey's mind, if there are any convictions in such a mind?"[114]

Most all of these supposed ancestral bones of man have been catalogued in a Time–Life book, *The Missing Link,* Volume 2 in the

111. Gould, S. J., *Natural History,* vol. 85, 1976, p. 30.
112. Kluger, Jeffrey, "Not So Extinct After All: The Primitive *Homo erectus* May Have Survived Long Enough to Coexist with Modern Humans," *Time,* 23 December 1996.
113. Wilford, John Noble, "3 Human Species Coexisted Eons Ago, New Data Suggest," *New York Times,* 13 December 1996.
114. Darwin, Charles, quoted in Francis Darwin (ed.), *Life and Letters of Charles Darwin* (1903; 1971 reprint), Vol. 1, p. 285.

"Emergence of Man Series," published in 1972. It has a complete listing of all the *australopithecine* finds up to the end of 1971.

Although over 1,400 specimens are given, most are little more than scraps of bone or isolated teeth. Not one complete skeleton of one individual exists. All that anthropologists have in their ancestral closet are bits and pieces.

"The fossils that decorate our family tree are so scarce that there are still more scientists than specimens. The remarkable fact is that all the physical evidence we have for human evolution can still be placed, with room to spare, inside a single coffin!"[115]

"The entire hominid collection known today would barely cover a billiard table. . . . The collection is so tantalizingly incomplete, and the specimens themselves often so fragmentary and inconclusive, that more can be said about what is missing than about what is present."[116]

"I don't want to pour too much scorn on paleontologists, but if you were to spend your life picking up bones and finding little fragments of head and little fragments of jaw, there's a very strong desire there to exaggerate the importance of those fragments."[117]

"The problem with a lot of anthropologists is that they want so much to find a hominid that any scrap of bone becomes a hominid bone."[118]

From grade school on up, children are taught about cavemen, *and are gradually conditioned to the idea that we evolved from lower forms of life. They are also taught about the bones and skulls of our "ancestors." As adults, we frequently hear reports of fossil remains of apelike humans that have been found. Each discovery has been hailed as a landmark proof of the theory of evolution.* Scientists have given a name to these supposed half–man/half–ape remains; they call them *hominids.*

115. *Science Digest 90,* May 1982, p. 44.

116. Reader, John, *New Scientist 89,* March 26, 1981, p. 802.

117. Kirby, Greg, address at meeting of Biology Teachers' Association, South Australia, 1976 [Flinders University professor].

118. White, Timothy, quoted in *New Scientist 98,* April 28, 1983, p. 199 [University of California anthropologist].

CHAPTER 13

ONE GIANT LEAP FOR MANKIND

E volutionists teach two variant theories regarding man's di-rect ancestor: (1) man and ape came from a common ancestor about 5 to 20 million years ago; (2) man descended from an ape. Modern man is said to have evolved about 100,000 years ago—and then he stopped evolving! It is claimed that, since that time, man has switched over from "physical evolution" to "cultural and social evolution." This is an attempt to explain the fact that, in historical records, evolution has never been known among humans.

There is no evidence that evolution is now occurring, or has ever occurred, among animals or plants. Are they culturally evolving now also? In addition, it is strange that if man is essentially the same as he was a million years ago, then why did he only begin leaving writings, buildings, and artifacts during the last few thousand years? Why does human history only go back less than 5,000 years?

"The search for the proverbial 'missing link' in man's evolution, that holy grail of a never–dying sect of anatomists and biologists, al-lows speculation and myth to flourish as happily today as they did 50 years ago and more."[119] Did man descend from the apes? Our DNA is different from that of each of the apes, monkeys, and all the rest. The number of vertebrae in our backbone is different from that in

---

119. Zukerman, Sir Solly, "Myth and Method in Anatomy," *Journal of the Royal College of Surgeons of Edinburgh* (1966), Vol. 11(2), pp. 87–114.

the apes. Our cranial (brain) capacity is totally different from the great apes.

Orangutans 275–500cc
Chimpanzees 275–500cc
Gorillas 340–752cc
Man 1100–1700cc

Cranial capacity is, by itself, an important test of whether a skull is from a man or an ape. "Since there are variations in tissues and fluids, the cranial capacity is never exactly equal to brain size, but can give an approximation. A skull's capacity is determined by pouring seeds or buckshot into the large hole at the base of the skull (*foramen magnum*), then emptying the pellets into a measuring jar. The volume is usually given in cubic centimeters (cc). Living humans have a cranial capacity ranging from about 950cc to 1,800cc, with the average about 1,400cc" (Milner, 1990, p. 98).

APES
Evolution teaches that we descended from the great apes and in turn, from the gibbons and other smaller apes. However, there are several differences between man and ape: (1) Birth weight as a percentage of maternal weight in man is almost twice that of the great apes (5.5 vs. 2.4–4.1), but about the same or less than that found in monkeys (5–10) and in gibbons (7.5). (2) Order of eruption of teeth is the same in man and in the Old World monkeys, but it is different from that of the great apes. (3) Walking upright is quite different. Man and the gibbon walk habitually upright; the great apes do not. (4) The neck hinge is at the back on man, but at the front on the ape.

As with the other teachings of evolution, scientific facts are on the side of the creationists. Evolutionists and their incredulous theories are outside the domain of scientific fact, discovery, and law. The shape and arrangement of the teeth, for example, is quite different for apes and man:

"Many male primates have large canine teeth, which are used in fighting and defense. Where the upper canines meet, or occlude, with the lower jaw, there are spaces, or gaps, between the opposing teeth. Canine *diastemas* [spaces opposite large canines] are characteristic of the jaws of baboons, gorillas, and monkeys. They are used as a diagnostic feature in studying fossils because they are absent in hominids [men or near-men]. A primate jaw with canine diastemas is considered probably related to apes or monkeys, not close to the human family" (Milner, 1990, p. 69).

HOMINID HOAXES

In an article about the grand opening of the International Louis Leakey Memorial Institute for African Prehistory (TILLMIAP) in Nairobi, Kenya, Lewin wrote this: "Perhaps more than any other science, human prehistory is a highly personalized pursuit, the whole atmosphere reverberating with the repeated collisions of oversized egos. The reasons are not difficult to discover. For a start, the topic under scrutiny—human origins—is highly emotional, and there are reputations to be made and public acclaim to be savored for people who unearth ever older putative human ancestors. But the major problem has been the pitifully small number of hominid fossils on which prehistorians exercise their imaginative talents."[120]

One problem is all that these experts have to work with are such things as jaw fragments, broken skull pieces, and parts of other bones. No complete (or even half-complete) skeleton linking man with the rest of the animals has ever been found. But, working with pieces collected here and there, imagination can produce most wonderful "discoveries." In some instances, some of the pieces have been found at a distance from the rest of the fragments.

PILTDOWN MAN

In 1912, *Piltdown man* was found. This created a great sensation in both the newspapers and halls of science when it was announced by the British Geological Society. They gave it the scientific name *Eoanthropus dawsoni*. For nearly 40 years, the scientific world bowed

---

120. Lewin, Roger, "A New Focus for African Prehistory," *New Scientist,* September 29, 1977, p. 793.

before Piltdown man as the great key to human evolution. Only one specimen existed, when there ought to be thousands if it was genuine. Paintings were made of the great men who found and worked on it, and three of those men were later knighted by the king of England. Such is the stuff of glory. Ignored was the report of a dentist in 1916 who said that the teeth had been filed down by someone.

In 1953, Joseph Weiner and Kenneth Oakley applied a recently developed fluorine test to the bones—and found that Piltdown man was a grand hoax! Someone had taken an ape jaw and put it with a

PILTDOWN MAN

Piltdown Man was accepted as the great "missing link" for 40 years until finally exposed as a fraud. Parts of a chimpanzee jaw and teeth had been carefully altered, and then combined with doctored parts of a human skull. Only a very few bones were used, to enable the fabricators to "reconstruct" the skull in the shape of an "ancestral man."

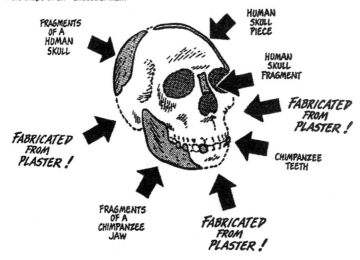

human skull, filed the teeth somewhat, and then carefully stained it all so that the bones looked both ancient and like a matching set. Imported mammalian fossils and handcrafted tools were placed nearby. It took 40 years to unravel that particular hoax.

> Careful examination of the bone pieces [in 1953] revealed the startling information that the whole thing was a fabrication, a hoax perpetrated by Dawson, probably, to achieve recognition. The skulls were collections of pieces, some human and some not. One skull had a human skull cap but an ape lower jaw. The teeth had

been filed and the front of the jaw broken off to obscure the simian [ape] origin. Some fragments used had been stained to hide the fact that the bones were not fossil, but fresh. In drilling into the bones, researchers obtained shavings rather than powder, as would be expected in truly fossilized bone.[121]

RHODESIAN MAN

Rhodesian man, frequently classified as *H. rhodesiensis, was* found in an iron and zinc mine in Broken Hill, Northern Rhodesia (now Kabwe, Zambia) in 1921 by Tom Zwiglaar, a Swiss miner. The find consisted of the bones of three or four family members: a man, a woman, and one or two children. The bones were dug out by a mining company and not by an experienced scientist, so much of the circumstances of their death and lifestyle are unknown. Only the skull of the man survived.

The skull shares many features with other fossil skulls that have been classified as *H. erectus* (upright man), a contrived species of man. This designation is now being hotly debated. Most anthropologists believe Rhodesian man to be within the group of *H. heidelbergensis,* though other designations such as archaic *H. sapiens* and *H. sapiens rhodesiensis* have also been proposed. The facial bones of Rhodesian man are the same as for any normal human being. These bones do not show any apelike features, such as a protruding muzzle.

A report in *New Scientist* dated January 16, 1993, entitled "On the Origin of Races" stated: "They are now proposing nothing less than the complete abolition of *H. erectus,* on the grounds that the species is insufficiently distinct from *H. sapiens.* All fossil remains of *H. erectus* and archaic *H. sapiens* (including Neanderthals) should be reclassified into a single species, *H. sapiens,* which is to be subdivided only into races." With this recommendation Rhodesian man is simply human.

Nevertheless, anthropologists and artists set to work, turning him into a half–ape/half–human sort of creature. Then a competent anatomist had the opportunity to examine it, and found that this was

---

121. Coffin, Harold G., *Creation: Accident or Design?* (1961), p. 221.

just a normal human being. Further analysis revealed dental caries which modern diets tend to produce, and also a hole through the skull made by a bullet or crossbow. So Rhodesian man is not so ancient after all.

TAUNG CHILD

Taung child refers to the fossil of a skull specimen of *Australopithecus africanus*. It was discovered in 1924 by Raymond Dart, a quarryman working for the Northern Lime Company in Taung, South Africa. He came across the front face and lower jaw of an immature ape in a cave in the Taung limestone quarry of South Africa and rushed to report it, accompanied by extravagant claims. A majority of scientists rejected this find, but the press loudly proclaimed it to be the "the missing link." However, when the Taung child was compared to an equivalent 9-year-old child, examinations suggested that *A. africanus'* growth rate to adolescence was the same as in modern apes like chimpanzees (genus Pan).

"Differences due to age are especially significant with reference to the structure of the skull in apes. Very pronounced changes occur during the transition from juvenile to adult in apes, but not in Man. The skull of a juvenile ape is somewhat different from that of Man. This juvenile skull should never have been compared to those of adult apes and humans."[122]

Today most experts dismiss it as the skull of a young ape.

NEBRASKA MAN

In 1922, Henry Fairfield Osborn, the director of the American Museum of Natural History, declared that he had found a molar tooth fossil in western Nebraska near Snake Brook belonging to the Pliocene period. *Hesperopithecus* meant "ape of the western world" and it was heralded as the first higher primate of North America. This tooth allegedly bore the common characteristics of both man and ape. Deep scientific arguments began in which some interpreted this

---

122. Gish, Duane, *Evolution: the Challenge of the Fossil Record* (1985), p. 178.

tooth to be that of *Pithecanthropus erectus* while others claimed it was closer to that of modern human beings. It was also immediately given a scientific name: *Hesperopithecus haroldcooki.*

Many authorities gave Osborn their support. Based on this single tooth, reconstructions of Nebraska man's head and body were drawn. Moreover, Nebraska man was even pictured with a whole family. An illustration of *H. haroldcooki* was done by artist Amedee Forestier, who modelled the drawing on the proportions of *Pithecanthropus* (now *H. erectus*), the "Java ape–man," for the *Illustrated News of London.* Osborn was not impressed with the illustration, calling it "*a figment of the imagination of no scientific value, and undoubtedly inaccurate.*" Grafton Smith, one of those involved in publicizing Nebraska man, was knighted for his efforts in making known this fabulous find.

Nebraska man was key evidence at the Scopes trial in July 1925 in Dayton, Tennessee. Henry F. Osborn, a leading paleontologist, ridiculed William Jennings Bryan at the trial, declaring that the tooth was "the herald of anthropoid apes in America," and that it "speaks volumes of truth."[123] Further fieldwork on the site in 1925 however revealed that the tooth was falsely identified. At the trial, two specialists in teeth at the American Museum of Natural History said that after careful study, the tooth was definitely from a species closer to man than to ape.[124] In 1927, other parts of the skeleton were also found. According to these newly discovered pieces, the tooth belonged neither to a man nor to an ape. It was realized that it belonged to an extinct species of wild American pig called *Prosthennops.* In 1972, living specimens of the same pig were found in Paraguay.

AUSTRALOPITHECINES

Australopithecus (southern ape) is the name given to a variety of ape bones found in Africa. Evolutionists claim that *Australopithecus* are the most primitive ancestors of modern men. These are an old species with a head and skull structure similar to that of modern apes,

---

123. Osborn, H. F., *Evolution and Religion in Education,* 1926, p. 103.
124. *Science 55,* May 5, 1922, p. 464.

yet with a smaller cranial capacity. According to the claims of evolutionists, these creatures have a very important feature that authenticates them as the ancestors of men: bipedalism. We will look at this in more detail later.

Australopithecus is nothing but an old ape species which varies in type that has become extinct. Some of them are robust, while others are small and slight. The fact of the matter is that the creatures called *Australopithecus* in this scenario fabricated by evolutionists are really apes that became extinct. Creatures in the *Homo* series are members of various human races that lived in the past and disappeared. Evolutionists arranged various ape and human fossils from the smallest to the biggest in order to form a "human evolution" scheme. Research however, has demonstrated that these fossils by no means imply an evolutionary process and that while some of these alleged ancestors of man were real apes, some of them were real humans.

After examining the bones carefully, anthropologists have gravely announced that they come from an ancient race of pre–people who supposedly lived from 1 to 4 million years ago. These bones have been found at various African sites, including Sterkfontein, Swartkrans, Koobi Fora, Olduvai, Hadar, and Orno River. The *australopithecines,* like modern apes, had a wide range of varieties. But they were all apes. Some experts believe that these apes, the *australopithecines,* descended from another ape, the *rāmapithecines (Ramapithecus* is

AUSTRALOPITHECUS

A comparative view of an Australopithecus, chimpanzee, and human skull. The Australopithecus is clearly an ape, and in no way a transition between ape and man.

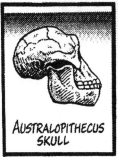
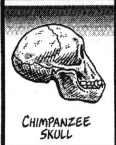
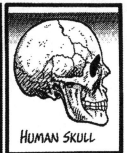

AUSTRALOPITHECUS SKULL

CHIMPANZEE SKULL

HUMAN SKULL

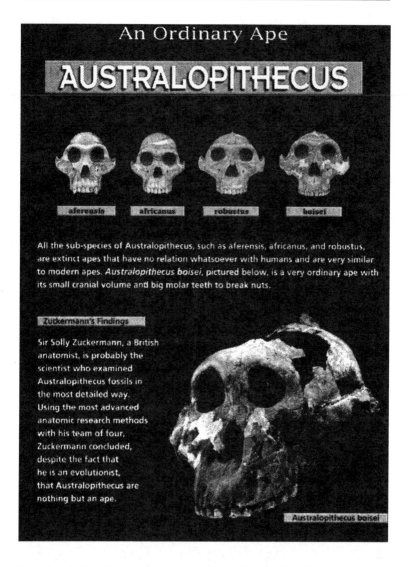

An Ordinary Ape

AUSTRALOPITHECUS

aferensis **africanus** **robustus** **boisei**

All the sub-species of Australopithecus, such as aferensis, africanus, and robustus, are extinct apes that have no relation whatsoever with humans and are very similar to modern apes. *Australopithecus boisei*, pictured below, is a very ordinary ape with its small cranial volume and big molar teeth to break nuts.

Zuckermann's Findings

Sir Solly Zuckermann, a British anatomist, is probably the scientist who examined Australopithecus fossils in the most detailed way. Using the most advanced anatomic research methods with his team of four, Zuckermann concluded, despite the fact that he is an evolutionist, that Australopithecus are nothing but an ape.

Australopithecus boisei

the singular), which is supposed to have lived 12 million years ago, though "no proven ancestor is known for any early *Australopithecus*, nor for any early *Homo* [*habilis*]."[125] One of the most famous was named "Lucy".

---

125. Mehlert, W., "The *Australopithecines* and (Alleged) Early Man," *Creation Research Society Quarterly,* June 1980, p. 25.

LUCY

Lucy, one of the most recent of the *Australopithecus* finds, was unearthed by Donald C. Johanson at Hadar, Ethiopia in 1975. He dated it at 3 million years B.P. [Before Present]. In 1979, Johanson and White claimed that Lucy came under an ape/man classification *(Australopithecus afarensis)*. But even before that startling announcement, the situation did not look too good for Lucy. In 1976, Johanson said that "Lucy has massive V-shaped jaws in contrast to man."[126] In 1981, he said that she was "embarrassingly un-*Homo* like" (*Science 81*, 2(2):53–55). *Time* magazine reported in 1977 that Lucy had a tiny skull, a head like an ape, a braincase size the same as that of a chimp (450cc) and "was surprisingly short legged."[127]

Dr. David Menton states in his article "Farewell to Lucy," "Three Israeli scientists have reported in the most recent issue of the *Proceedings of the National Academy of Science* that *Au. afarensis* may not be our ancestor at all. It all hinges on the jaw of these creatures (pardon the pun). Alas, *Au. afarensis* has a lower jaw bone (mandible) that closely resembles that of a gorilla—not that of a human or even a chimp. The scientists conclude that this 'cast[s] doubt on the role of *Au. afarensis* as a modern human ancestor.'"[128]

Dr. Yves Coppens, appearing on BBC-TV in 1982, stated that Lucy's skull was like that of an ape. In 1983, Jeremy Cherfas said that Lucy's ankle bone *(talus)* tilts backward like a gorilla, instead of forward as in human beings who need it so to walk upright, and concluded that the differences between her and human beings are "unmistakable."[129] Susman and Stern of New York University carefully examined Lucy and said her thumb was apelike, her toes long and curved for tree climbing, and "she probably nested in the trees and lived like other monkeys."[130] Several scientists have decided that the bones of Lucy come from two different sources. Commenting on this,

126. *National Geographic Magazine,* 150:790–810.
127. *Time,* November 7, 1979, pp. 68–69.
128. Menton, Dr. David, "Farewell to Lucy", Vol. 104, pp. 6568–6572, AiG-US, April 18, 2007.
129. Cherfas, J., *New Scientist,* (97:172 [1982].
130. *Bible Science Newsletter,* 1982, p. 4.

Peter Andrews of the British Museum of Natural History said this: "To complicate matters further, some researchers believe that the *afarensis* sample [Lucy] is really a mixture of two separate species. The most convincing evidence for this is based on characteristics of the knee and elbow joints."[131]

Regarding those knee joints, Owen Lovejoy, Richard Leakey's highly qualified associate (an anatomist), declared at a 1979 lecture in the United States that a multivariate analysis of Lucy's knee joints revealed her to be an ape. So whether Lucy's bones belong to one creature or two, they are both apes.

Johanson's theory about Lucy is based on an assumption linking two fossils a thousand miles apart:

Although the Lucy fossils were initially dated at 3 million years, Johanson had announced them as 3.5 million because he said the species was "the same" as a skull found by Mary Leakey at Laetoli, Tanzania. By proposing Mary Leakey's find as the "type specimen"

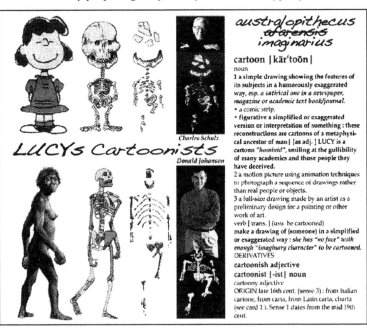

LUCY's Cartoonists

Charles Schulz

Donald Johanson

australopithecus afarensis imaginarius

cartoon | kär'toōn |
noun
1 a simple drawing showing the features of its subjects in a humorously exaggerated way, esp. a satirical one in a newspaper, magazine or academic text book/journal.
• a comic strip.
• figurative a simplified or exaggerated version or interpretation of something : these reconstructions are cartoons of a metaphysical ancestor of man | [as adj.] LUCY is a cartoon "hominid", smiling at the gullibility of many academics and those people they have deceived.
2 a motion picture using animation techniques to photograph a sequence of drawings rather than real people or objects.
3 a full-size drawing made by an artist as a preliminary design for a painting or other work of art.
verb | trans.] (usu. be cartooned)
make a drawing of (someone) in a simplified or exaggerated way : she has "no face" with enough "imaginary character" to be cartooned.
DERIVATIVES
cartoonish adjective
cartoonist | -ist | noun
cartoony adjective
ORIGIN late 16th cent. (sense 3) : from Italian cartone, from carta, from Latin carta, charta (see card 1). Sense 1 dates from the mid 19th cent.

131. Andrews, Peter, "The Descent of Man," *New Scientist,* 102:24 (1984).

for *Australopithecus afarensis,* he was identifying Lucy with another fossil 1,000 miles [1,609 km] from the Afar [in northern Ethiopia] and half a million years older! Mary thought the two not at all the same and refused to have any part of linking her specimen with [Johanson's] *afarensis.* . . . She announced that she strongly resented Johanson's "appropriating" her find, her reputation, and the older date to lend authority to Lucy. Thus began the bitter, persistent feud between Johanson and the Leakeys.

—Milner, 1990, p. 285

Johanson, himself, finally decided that Lucy was only an ape. "Johanson himself originally described the fossils as *Homo,* a species of man, but soon after changed his mind based on the assessment of his colleague, Tim White. They now describe the bones as too apelike in the jaws, teeth and skull to be considered *Homo,* yet also sufficiently distinct from other, later *australopithecines* to warrant their own species" (*ibid.*).

Speaking of the *australopithecines,* J. S. Weiner commented: "The apelike profile of *Australopithecus* is so pronounced that its outline can be superimposed on that of a female chimpanzee with a remarkable closeness of fit, and in this respect and others it stands in strong contrast to modern man."[132]

In 1957, Ashley Montagu, a leading U.S. anthropologist, wrote that these extremely apelike creatures could not possibly have anything to do with man.[133]

Mehlert sums it up. "The evidence . . . makes it overwhelmingly likely that Lucy was no more than a variety of pigmy chimpanzee, and walked the same way (awkwardly upright on occasions, but mostly quadrupedal). The 'evidence' for the alleged transformation from ape to man is extremely unconvincing."[134]

After the most careful research, Oxnard and Zuckerman have

---

132. Weiner, J. S., *The Natural History of Man* (1973).

133. Montegu, A., *Man's First Million Years.*

134. Mehlert, A. W., news note, *Creation Research Society Quarterly,* December 1985, p. 145.

come to the conclusion that *Australopithecus* is an ape; it is not a transition between the two.

> Dr. Charles Oxnard and Sir Solly Zuckerman were leaders in the development of a powerful multivariate analysis procedure. This computerized technique simultaneously performs millions of comparisons on hundreds of corresponding dimensions of the bones of living apes, humans, and the *australopithecines.* Their verdict, that the *australopithecines* are not intermediate between man and living apes, is quite different from the more subjective and less analytical visual techniques of most anthropologists. This technique, however, has not yet been applied to the most recent type of *australopithecine*, commonly known as "Lucy."
> —Brown, 1989, p. 39

Consequently, Oxnard's multivariate analysis showed that Lucy could not possibly be an intermediate missing link between humans and knuckle–walking apelike ancestors. He found that the *australo-pithecine* fossils "clearly differ more from both humans and African apes, than do these two living groups from each other. The *australo-pithecines* are unique."[135]

NUTCRACKER MAN

Nutcracker man was found in 1959 by Louis Leakey in the Olduvai Gorge in East Africa, and is one of the *australopithecines* discussed above. Since the Leakeys are frequently mentioned in articles about the bones of man's ancestors, we will here mention that Louis Leakey was born in Africa, the son of a missionary. He and his wife Mary both had doctorates. After his death, his son Richard continued bone hunting with his mother. Olduvai Gorge is located in East Africa, about 100 miles west of Mount Kilimanjaro. It consists of a 300–foot

---

135. Oxnard, C. E., *Fossils, Sex and Teeth—New Perspectives on Human Evolution,* University of Washington Press, Seattle and London, p. 227, 1987. Oxnard had previously concluded much the same about *Australopithecus* africanus, *Nature,* 258:389–395, 1975.

gorge that has cut through five main horizontal beds.

Louis Leakey called his find *Zinjanthropus boisei,* but the press called it "Nutcracker man" because it had a jaw much larger than the skull. This was probably another case of mismatched skull parts. The skull was very apelike, but some tools were nearby, so Leakey decided that it had to be half–human. Slim evidence, but that is how it goes in the annals of evolutionary science. When he first announced it, Leakey declared that it was the earliest man, and was 600,000 years old! Although the age was a guess, it came just as funds from Charles Boise ran out. A new sponsor was needed, and the *National Geographic Society* stepped in and has funded the Leakey's ever since.

In 1961, the skull of Nutcracker man was dated by the notoriously inaccurate potassium–argon method at 1.75 million years. That story really made the headlines! In 1968, the same materials were dated by carbon–14, which, although quite inaccurate, is far safer than potassium–argon. The C14 dating of Nutcracker man was only 10,100 years. But there is more: A complete, fully human skeleton was discovered in 1913 by the German anthropologist Hans Reck, just above the later find of Nutcracker man.

There was much discussion of these remains and Louis Leakey personally examined them in the 1930s. But in his 1959 press announcement, he made no mention of them. To do so would have ruined his announced discovery. C14 tests on the skull that Reck found (the rest of the skeleton had disappeared from the Munich museum) were made in 1974 and yielded a date of 16,920 years. Although radiocarbon dating can have a wide margin of error, 16,920 is far different from 1.75 million! Eventually Leakey conceded that Nutcracker man was just another ape skull, like Dart's Taung man.

In 1964, another skull—this one belonging to a human—was found near those same tools that Leakey found in 1959. One of its "hand bones" was later found to be a piece of a human rib.

SKULL 1470

In 1972, Richard Leakey announced what he thought to be a humanlike fossil skull, and gave it an astonishing date of 2.8 million years. The official name of this find is *KNM-ER 1470,* but it is commonly known as "Skull 1470." If this is a human skull, then it would pre-date all the man/ape bones said to be its ancestors. Both Leakey and others think it looks essentially like a modern small-brained person. It was pieced together from several fragments. In 1972, Bernard Ngeneo, of Richard Leakey's "Hominid Gang," found a similar but much more complete skull at East Turkana. It is generally known as the "1470" skull, from its accession number at the Kenya National Museum.

> The 1470 skull was pieced together by Richard Leakey's wife Meave and several anatomists from dozens of fragments—a jigsaw puzzle that took six weeks to assemble. Dated at 1.89 million years old, with a cranial capacity of 750cc, Leakey believes it is the oldest fossil of a true human ancestor. In his view, the *australopithecines* and other hominid fossils were side-branches.
>
> Leakey fought hard to win a place for his 1470 (along with the previous habiline fragments found at Olduvai) because most anthropologists thought the skull was simply "too modern-looking" to be as ancient as he at first claimed.
>
> —Milner, 1990, p. 217

Here was Leakey's original announcement in regard to this skull: "Either we toss out this skull or we toss out our theories of early man.... [It] leaves in ruins the notion that all early fossils can be arranged in an orderly sequence of evolutionary change."[136]

But it should be understood that modern, living, small-brained (750cc) human beings have existed; so the finding of a 750cc Skull 1470 is no reason to think it is an ancestor of mankind.

"Human qualities of mind, Keith proclaimed, can only appear when brain volume is at least 750 cubic centimeters, a point nick-named 'Keith's rubicon' (dividing line). How did he arrive at the 'magic' number of 750cc? It was the smallest functioning modern human brain anatomists had seen at the time [when Sir Arthur

---

136. Leakey, Richard E., "Skull 1470," *National Geographic,* June 1973, p. 819.

Keith, one of those involved in the Piltdown hoax, was alive earlier in this century]" (Milner, 1990, p. 249).

Early comments on Skull 1470 included these:

"The finding of 'Skull 1470,' which Richard Leakey says is nearly 3 million years old and really human, will shatter the whole evolutionary story built upon so-called hominoids, if anthropologists accept Leakey's pronouncements. An artist for the *National Geographic Magazine* obligingly painted a reconstruction which is very human indeed. The only thing peculiar is the overly flat nose—and the shape of the nose cannot be ascertained from a skull."[137]

"The latest reports of Richard Leakey are startling, and, if verified, will reduce to a shambles the presently held schemes of evolutionists concerning man's origins."[138]

After considering the implications of the situation, the skull was carefully re-dated, lest it be thought that human beings had lived 2.8 million years ago. The experts did not want it to predate its ancestors! "The 1470 Skull discovered by Richard Leakey in 1972 was originally 'dated' at 2.6 million years. However, many anthropologists objected because then the more modern 1470 Skull would predate all its supposed ancestors. Thus 1470 was 're-dated' until a more 'acceptable' estimate of 1.8 million years was adopted."[139]

This skull may have been that of a microcephalic human, a teenage human, or an ape. It lacks the prominent eyebrow ridges common to *H. erectus* (Java man, etc.), many Neanderthals, and *Australopithecus.* Some fossil apes had brow ridges; others lacked them. The brow ridge slopes back abruptly as does that of simians (apes), but it is somewhat more rounded. The size of the braincase is equivalent to that of a teenager, or a microcephalic, and somewhat larger than an ape: 775cc. A gorilla averages 500cc, and an *Australopithecus* only 422-530cc. The average brain size for modern man is 1450cc. But there are exceptions to this: Microcephalics are human beings

---

137. News note, *Creation Research Society Quarterly,* September 1974, p. 131.

138. Gish, Duane T., *Evolution: The Fossils Say No!* (1973), p. 105.

139. Moore, John N., "Teaching About Origin Questions: Origin of Human Beings," *Creation Research Society Quarterly,* March 1986, p. 185.

which have brains as small as 775cc. This condition is a birth defect which, though unfortunate, occurs from time to time. "Humans with microcephaly are quite subnormal in intelligence, but they still show specifically human behavioral patterns."[140]

"None of these early hominids had brains approaching the size of modern human ones. The indices of encephalization show that *australopithecines* were only slightly above the great apes in relative brain size and even the largest cranium [Skull 1470] is about as close to apes as it is to humans."[141]

It is significant that the lower jaw was not found. This would have told a lot. The face of the skull, below the eyes, protrudes forward in the manner of apes. The jaw and molars are somewhat larger than the average modern human's, but not larger than those of some people. There appears to be a lack of bony support beneath the nostrils, such as is found in gorillas. Facial skeletons are relatively larger in apes than the braincase size. Skull 1470 is about midway in this category, and thus not like that of humans. It also has a long upper lip area, such as apes have. Viewing three skulls from the rear (an adult human, Skull 1470, and *Australopithecus),* we find that Skull 1470 has similarities to that of *Australopithecus.*

John Cuozzo, in a four-page report complete with two drawings and seven photographs (*Creation Research Society Quarterly,* December 1977, pp. 173–176), provides intriguing evidence for his contention that Skull 1470 may have been that of an early teenage human being, and that damage to the skull after death caused the apelike characteristics in the nasal opening, etc. Frankly, there is not enough data available to say much more. There is no doubt that the special human qualities of speech, and so forth, would not reveal themselves in a skull.

It is also a fact that evolutionists eagerly desire evidence that man descended from an apelike ancestor. Yet over 100 years of

140. Lubenow, Marvin, "Evolutionary Reversals: the Latest Problem Facing Stratigraphy and Evolutionary Phylogeny," *Bible-Science Newsletter,* 14{11}:1–4 (1976).
141. McHenry, Henry M., "Fossils and the Mosaic Nature of Human Evolution," *Science* 190(4213):425–431.

searching has not disclosed this even though millions of fossils have been dug out of the ground and examined. If mankind had indeed descended from another creature, there should be abundant fossil evidence. But it is not there.

The next step in the imaginary human evolution is *"Homo,"* that is, the human series. These living beings are humans who are no different from modern men, yet who have some racial differences. Seeking to exaggerate these differences, evolutionists represent these people not as a race of modern man but as a different species. However, as you will soon see, the people in the *Homo* series are nothing but ordinary human racial types.

According to the fanciful scheme of evolutionists, the internal imaginary evolution of the *Homo* species is as follows: First *H. habilis*, then *H. erectus*, then *H. sapiens* archaic and Neanderthal man, later Cro–Magnon man, and finally modern man. Despite the claims of evolutionists to the contrary, all the species we have enumerated above are nothing but genuine human beings. Let us first examine *H. habilis*, who evolutionists refer to as the most primitive human species.

CHAPTER 14

The Genus Homo

Homo habilis or "tool using man" is another ape. In the 1960s, Louis Leakey found some teeth and skull fragments at Olduvai. He dated them at 1.8 million years ago and decided they belonged to the human family, therefore naming them *Homo*. But many anthropologists have clearly shown that *habilis* was nothing more than a large–brained *Australopithecus* ape.

Human beings have a brain size of about 1500cc (cubic centimeters). In contrast, *habilis* was 660cc. Other brain sizes would be 800cc for Hadar, 900cc for Koobi Fora. Most other brain sizes are about 500cc. The Taung and Sterkfontein skulls are around 430cc apiece, so an adult of their species would only be 550–600cc. Thus on the score of size of braincase, these finds prove nothing. An excellent and detailed article on this, which includes 13 charts and graphs, are found in "Some Implications of Variant Cranial Capacities for the Best–preserved Australopithecine Skull Specimens" by Gerald Duffert.[142] The article reveals that there was evidence of fraudulent measurements of those ancient African skulls. Repeatedly, an initial measurement of a high cubic centimeter volume was announced for the skull, but later measurements by other investigators disclosed much smaller measurements! "Overall, the revisionary calculations of *australopithecine* skulls have led to reductions of their calculated volumes. The total percentage differences amount to –157.91."[143]

"The hypothesis that brain enlargement marked the beginning

---

142. *Creation Research Society Quarterly,* September 1983, pp. 96–104
143. Ibid., pp. 100

A Contemporary Human Race

HOMO ERECTUS

Homo erectus, which is repetitively misrepresented as a transitional form by evolutionists, is in fact a contemporary human race.

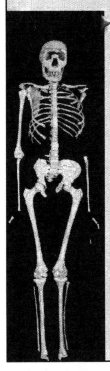

Tall and modern "Turkana Boy" fossil. The modern skeletal structure of this fossil, which was claimed to be 2 million years old, upset all evolutionists. Even Richard Leakey, a prominent evolutionist, said: "he would probably go unnoticed in a crowd today"

The best indication that Homo erectus is no different from humans is that he lived till very recent times. Top and left, 10-20 thousand-year-old Australia Kow Swamp fossils. Below is the reconstruction of a 20 thousand-year-old Homo erectus skull unearthed in Java published in Time Magazine.

Evolutionists represent Homo erectus fossils like Java Man and Peking Man as primitive transitional forms. This claim is mainly based on the respectively lower cranial volumes of these skulls compared to the average cranial volume of our day. However, in our day, there still exist some races having the same cranial volume as that of Homo erectus.

of man was long popular, but went out of fashion with the discovery that the endocranial volumes of the *australopithecine* group were not larger than those of gorillas."[144]

Homo Erectus

As the name implies, *H. erectus* means "man who walks upright."

---

144. Simons, Elwin L., *Primate Evolution: An Introduction to Man's Place in Nature* (1972), p. 278.

Evolutionists have had to separate these fossils from earlier ones by adding the qualification of "erectness," because all the available *H. erectus* fossils are straight to an extent not observed in any of the *australopithecines* or so-called *H. habilis* specimens. There is no difference between the postcranial skeleton of modern man and that of *H. erectus*.

The primary reason for evolutionists' defining *H. erectus* as "primitive" is the cranial capacity of its skull (900–1,100cc), which is smaller than the average modern man, and its thick eyebrow projections. However, there are many people living today in the world who have the same cranial capacity as *H. erectus* (pygmies, for instance) and other races have protruding eyebrows (Native Australians, for instance). It is a commonly agreed-upon fact that differences in cranial capacity do not necessarily denote differences in intelligence or abilities. Intelligence depends on the internal organization of the brain, rather than on its volume.[145]

It is now a more pronounced fact in the scientific community that *H. erectus* is a superfluous taxon, and that fossils assigned to the *H. erectus* class are actually not so different from *H. sapiens* as to be considered a different species. In *American Scientist,* the discussions over this issue and the result of a conference held on the subject in 2000 were summarized in this way:

Most of the participants at the Senckenberg conference got drawn into a debate over the taxonomic status of *H. erectus* started by Milford Wolpoff of the University of Michigan, Alan Thorne of the University of Canberra, and their colleagues. They argued forcefully that *H. erectus* had no validity as a species and should be eliminated altogether. All members of the genus *Homo,* from about 2 million years ago to the present, were one highly variable, widely spread species, *H. sapiens*, with no natural breaks or subdivisions. The subject of the conference, *H. erectus*, didn't exist.[146]

---

145. Lubenow, Marvin, *Bones of Contention: a creationist assessment of the human fossils,* Baker Books, 1992, p. 83.

146. Shipman, Pat, "Doubting Dmanisi," *American Scientist,* November– December 2000, p. 491.

The conclusion reached by the scientists defending the above-mentioned thesis can be summarized as "*H. erectus* is not a different species from *H. sapiens*, but rather a race within *H. sapiens*." On the other hand, there is a huge gap between *H. erectus*, a human race, and the apes that preceded *H. erectus* in the "human evolution" scenario (*Australopithecus*, *H. habilis*, and *H. rudolfensis*). This means that the first men appeared in the fossil record suddenly and without any prior evolutionary history.

The most striking evidence showing that *H. erectus* is not a primitive species is the fossil of *Turkana boy*, one of the supposed oldest *H. erectus* remains. The upright skeletal structure of the fossil is no different from that of modern man. Its tall and slender skeletal structure complies with that of the people living in tropical regions in our day. This fossil is one of the most important pieces of evidence that *H. erectus* is simply another specimen of the modern human race.

Evolutionist Richard Leakey compares *H. erectus* and modern man as follows: "One would also see differences in the shape of the skull, in the degree of protrusion of the face, the robustness of the brows and so on. These differences are probably no more pronounced than we see today between the separate geographical races of modern humans. Such biological variation arises when populations are geographically separated from each other for significant lengths of time."[147]

Leakey means to say that the difference between *H. erectus* and us is no more than the difference between Africans and Eskimos. The cranial features of *H. erectus* resulted from their manner of feeding, from genetic emigration, and from their not assimilating with other human races for a lengthy period.

Another strong piece of evidence that *H. erectus*, made known to the entire world by the fossils of Peking man and Java man in Asia, is not a primitive species is found in the fossils of this species. According to an article published in *Time* magazine, *H. erectus* fossils aged 27,000 years were found on the island of Java. Again, in the

---

147. Leakey, Richard, *The Making of Mankind*, Sphere Books, London, 1981, p. 116.

Kow swamp in Australia, some 13,000-year-old fossils were found that bore *H. sapiens/H. erectus* characteristics. However, in time it was realized that these two fossils are not reliable. All these fossils demonstrate is that *H. erectus* continued living up to times very close to our day and were nothing but a human race that has since been buried in history.

JAVA MAN

In 1891, Java man was found. This is a classic instance of a man searching for evidence to support a theory. Eugene Dubois became a convinced evolutionist while attending a Dutch college. Dropping out of school, he began searching for fossils in Sumatra and other Dutch East Indies islands. He shipped thousands of crates of regular animal bones back to Holland and then went to Java. In September 1891 near the village of Trinil in a damp place by the Solo River, Dubois found a skull cap. A year later and 50 feet from where he had found the skull cap, he found a femur. Later he found three teeth in another location in that area. Dubois assumed that (1) all these bones were from the same individual, and (2) that they were as much as a million years old.

Incidentally, nearby, in the same condition (indicating the same approximate age), he also found two human skulls (known as the *Wadjak skulls),* but he did not publicize this find, for they had a cra-

JAVA MAN

The bone fragments known as "Java Man" came from an area known to have humans buried there. In the illustration below, notice that the Java Man bone fragments could either fit a human being (Von Koenigswald's reconstruction on the left) or a gorilla (reconstruction on the right). The Germans later decided they were from a human, and Dubois finally announced they were from a gibbon.

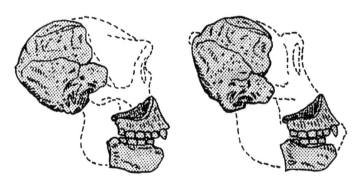

nial capacity somewhat above that of modern man. Thirty-one years later, in 1922, he admitted the Wadjaks skull were apes.

Excitedly, Dubois reported the find (the pieces of bone) as "Java man," and spent the rest of his life promoting this great discovery. The thigh bone was a normal human upper leg bone. As might be expected, many experts questioned whether all the bones came from the same person, though they said they were human bones, not ape bones. But Dubois spent most of the remainder of his life lecturing and telling people about the "half-human/half-ape" bones that he had found in Java in 1891-1892. He named it *Pithecanthropus erectus* (erect ape-man).

British zoologists thought it was human, German experts decided it was ape, and the French conjectured that it was something between the two. Finally, in 1907 a German expedition was sent from Berlin to Java to settle the matter. But Dubois would not show them his bone collection nor help them in any way. Arriving in Java, they went over the Trinil site thoroughly, removed 1,379 cubic yards of material and 43 boxfuls of bones, and then declared it all to be wasted time. Their main discovery was that Dubois' Java man bones had been taken from a depth that came from a nearby volcano. It had overflowed in the recent past and spewed forth lava, which overwhelmed and buried a number of people and animals.

About 15 years before his death and after most evolutionists had become convinced that his find was nothing more than bones from a modern human, Dubois announced his conviction that the bones belonged to a gibbon. School textbooks and popular books for the public continue to cite 500,000 years as the age of Java man, which, admittedly, is quite an imaginary figure.

PEKING MAN

Peking man emerged on the international scene in the 1920s. The finances of Davidson Black were just about running out and he needed help when, in 1927, he found a tooth near Peking, China. The Rockefeller Foundation stepped forward and gave him $80,000 to continue research on this colossal find. So Black continued looking and came up with a skull, copies of which are displayed today in biology laboratories. Black named it *Sinanthropus pekinensis* ("China man from Peking"), and received honors from all over the world for his discovery. After his death in 1934, the Jesuit that helped prepare Piltdown man (Teilhard de Chardin) took over the work at the site. Then Franz Weidenreich led, until all work stopped in 1936 because of the Japanese invasion of China.

This turned out to be some kind of town garbage dump. Although thousands of animal bones were found in this pit near Peking, only a few human skulls were found, and there was no evidence that they had evolved from anything else—even though there was 150 feet of animal bones in the pit. These human bones totaled 14 skulls in varying conditions, 11 jawbones, 147 teeth, and a couple of small arm bone and femur fragments, along with stone tools and carbon ash from fires. These were human bones, but with a somewhat smaller brain capacity (1,000cc, which some people today have), and with the prominent brow ridges which we find in Neanderthals and *Australopithecus*.

There are races today with larger brow ridges, including some Philippine women, which only men generally have. Patterns vary, but the species remains one. "The heavy-boned [Peking] hominid skull featured prominent brow ridges and a somewhat smaller braincase (about 1,000cc) than modern humans (1,500cc)" (Milner, 1990, p. 359).

A braincase of 1,000cc is not subhuman; people today vary between 1,000 and 2,000cc, with an occasional low of 750cc, and an average of 1,500–1,600cc. All of the Peking skulls disappeared during World War II, so we cannot now examine them with modern methods to check their genuineness.

Amidst the uncertainties of war-torn Beijing [earlier called Peking], it proved impossible to store them [Peking man bones] safely with Chinese authorities, so Weidenreich finally packed them for military shipment to the United States. They were believed to be aboard the marine ship *U.S.S. President Harrison,* which was sunk in the Pacific in mid–November 1941. So Peking man's bones may now be resting on the ocean's bottom.

Peking man was represented mainly by skulls—hardly any postcranial material. Not a pelvis or a rib; just skulls. Twenty years later, in the 1950s, Ernst Mayr came up with a new name, *H. erectus,* and then put a variety of bone finds (Java man, Peking man, and several others) into it.

Archaic Homo Sapiens

Archaic *H. sapiens* is the immediate forerunner of contemporary man in the imaginary evolutionary scheme. In fact, evolutionists do not have much to say about these men, as there are only minor differences between them and modern men. Some researchers even state that representatives of this race are still living today, and point to the aborigines in Australia as an example. Like *H. sapiens*, the aborigines also have thick protruding eyebrows, an inward–inclined mandibular structure, and a slightly smaller cranial volume. Moreover, significant discoveries have been made hinting that such people lived in Hungary and in some villages in Italy until not very long ago.

Evolutionists point to human fossils unearthed in the Neander valley of Holland which have been named Neanderthal man. Many contemporary researchers define Neanderthal man as a subspecies of modern man and call it *"H. sapiens neandertalensis."*

Neanderthals (cavemen)

The first introduction many children have to evolution is pictures of dinosaurs and cavemen. It is true that there have been groups that have lived in caves. They wandered from warm climates to colder ones and chose to live in caves for a time before building themselves homes in a new land. But the fact that some people lived in caves for awhile does not prove evolution from one species to another.

Diodorus Siculus, writing about 60 B.C., told of people living along the shores of the Red Sea in caves. He describes many other barbarian tribes, some of them quite primitive. Thus we see that both advanced civilizations and more backward cave cultures lived at the same time. We have no reason to conclude that the less advanced peoples were ancestors of the more advanced ones.

Archaeologists tell us that in some places in Palestine, people resembling the Neanderthal race lived in caves while not far away in Jericho people dwelt in well–built, beautifully decorated houses.

Evolutionists call the cavemen Neanderthals. In 1856 workers blasted a cave in the Neander Valley near Düsseldorf, Germany. Inside they found limb bones, pelvis, ribs, and a skull cap. The bones were examined by both scientists and evolutionists, and, for a number of years, all agreed that these were normal human beings. Even that ardent evolutionist and defender of Darwin, Thomas H. Huxley, said they belonged to people and did not prove evolution. Rudolph Virchow, a German anatomist, said the bones were those of modern men afflicted with rickets and arthritis. Many scientists today recognize that they had bowed legs due to rickets, caused by a lack of sunlight.

In 1886, two similar skulls were found at Spy, Belgium. In the early 1900s, a number of similar specimens were found in southern France. Over 100 specimens are now in collections. A French paleontologist named Marcellin Boule said they belonged to apelike creatures, but he was severely criticized for this even by other evolutionists who said this fossil was just modern man *(H. sapiens)*, deformed by arthritis. A most excellent, detailed analysis of how rickets and arthritis caused the features peculiar to Neanderthals was written

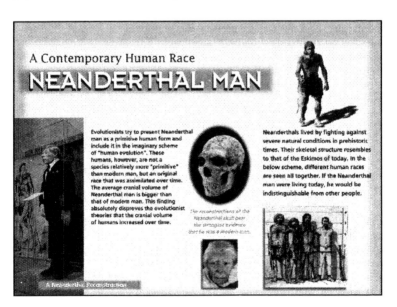

A Contemporary Human Race

NEANDERTHAL MAN

Evolutionists try to present Neanderthal man as a primitive human form and include it in the imaginary scheme of "human evolution". These humans, however, are not a species relatively more "primitive" than modern man, but an original race that was assimilated over time. The average cranial volume of Neanderthal man is bigger than that of modern man. This finding absolutely disproves the evolutionist theories that the cranial volume of humans increased over time.

The reconstructions of the Neanderthal skull over the strongest evidence that he was a modern man.

Neanderthals lived by fighting against severe natural conditions in prehistoric times. Their skeletal structure resembles to that of the Eskimos of today, in the below scheme, different human races are seen all together. If the Neanderthal man were living today, he would be indistinguishable from other people.

A Neanderthal Reconstruction

by Ivanhoe in a 1970 issue of the scientific journal *Nature*. The article is entitled "Was Virchow Right About Neanderthal?"

"Neanderthal man may have looked like he did, not because he was closely related to the great apes, but because he had rickets, an article in the British publication *Nature* suggests. The diet of Neanderthal man was definitely lacking in Vitamin D."[148]

Neanderthal features include a somewhat larger brow ridge (the *supra orbital torus)*, but it is known that arthritis can make this more prominent. Virchow noted that the thighbone *(femur)* was curved, a condition common to rickets. Lack of Vitamin D causes osteomalacia and rickets, producing a subtle facial change by increasing the size of the eye cavity *(orbit)*, especially vertically. D. J. M. Wright, in 1973, showed that congenital syphilis could also have caused the kind of bone deformities found in Neanderthal specimens.

The Neanderthals apparently lived at a time when there was not as much sunlight. We know that the Ice Age came as a result of worldwide volcanic dust pollution. The weather in Europe at that time was cold enough that they may have stayed so much in their caves that they did not obtain enough sunlight, especially due to the overcast sky conditions. They may also have lived longer than men do today. Biblical records indicate that those living just after the flood (on down to Abraham and even Moses) had somewhat longer life spans than we do today. In 1973, H. Israel explained that certain living individuals today begin to develop Neanderthaloid features—the heavy eyebrow ridges, elongated cranial vault, and so on—with extreme age. There is definite evidence that the Neanderthals were several hundred years old.

For more information, see the book *Buried Alive* by Jack Cuozzo (1998). In it, he clearly shows that the Neanderthals were several hundred years old. Facial bones keep growing throughout life. He also discovered that the evolutionists had mismatched the upper and lower jaw in order to make the Neanderthals look like apes.

Here are some facts you will not find in the textbooks: (1) In 1908 a typical Neanderthal skeleton was found in Poland. It had

---

148. "Neanderthals had Rickets," *Science Digest,* February 1971, p. 35.

been buried in a suit of chain armor that was not yet fully rusted.[149] (2) A Neanderthal skeleton was found in the Philippine islands in 1910. Due to the extreme moisture of that land, it would be impossible for the skeleton to be as much as a century old.[150] (3) A third interesting fact is that the Neanderthals had larger craniums than we do. They had larger brains! This indicates regression of our race from a former longer-lived, more intelligent race rather than evolutionary progression. Brain capacity is an important indicator of whether a cranium (the part of the skull which encloses the brain) belongs to an ape or a person.

"The cranial capacity of the Neanderthal race of *H. sapiens* was, on the average, equal to or even greater than that in modern man."[151]

"Normal human brain size is 1450cc-1500cc. Neanderthal's is 1600cc. If his brow is low, his brain is larger than modern man's."[152]

"The [Neanderthal] brain case on the average was more than 13 percent larger than that of the average of modern man."[153]

They also had well-developed culture, art, and religion. At the present time, most scientists agree that Neanderthals were just plain people that lived in caves for a time. Unfortunately, we are still waiting for this change in thinking to be seen in children's textbooks. Two Neanderthal-like skulls were found in Santa Barbara, California, in 1923. Researchers recognized that they were just Indian skulls. Neanderthals were just racial types similar to us.

CRO—MAGNON MAN

In 1868 a cave was discovered at Les Eyzies, in the Dordogne area of France. In the local dialect, *cro-magnon* means "big hole." A number of skeletons have been found there, and have been hailed as the great "missing link" between man and ape. The Cro-Magnons were

---

149. "Neanderthal in Armour," *Nature,* April 23, 1908, p. 587.
150. "Living Neanderthal Man," *Nature,* December 8, 1910, p. 176.
151. Dobzhansky, Theodosius, "Changing Man," *Science,* January 27, 1967, p. 410.
152. Pitman, Michael, *Adam and Evolution* (1984), p. 87.
153. von Fange, Erich A., "Time Upside Down," *Creation Research Society Quarterly,* June 1974, p. 23.

truly human, possibly of a noble bearing. Some were over six feet tall, with a cranial volume somewhat larger than that of men today. This means they had more brains than men have today. Not only did they have some excellent artists among them, but they also kept astronomy records. The Cro–Magnons were normal people, not monkeys, and they provide no evidence of a transition from ape to man.

The group characterized as *H. heidelbergensis* in evolutionist literature is in fact the same as archaic *H. sapiens*. The reason why two different terms are used to define the same human racial type is because of disagreements among evolutionists. All the fossils included under the *H. heidelbergensis* classification suggest that people who were anatomically very similar to modern Europeans lived 500,000 and even 740,000 years ago, first in England and then in Spain.

It is estimated that Cro–Magnon man lived 30,000 years ago. He has a dome–shaped cranium and a broad forehead. His cranium of 1,600cc is above the average for contemporary man. His skull has thick eyebrow projections and a bony protrusion at the back that is characteristic of both Neanderthal man and *H. erectus*.

Although the Cro–Magnon is considered to be a European race, the structure and volume of Cro–Magnon's cranium look very much like those of some races living in Africa and the tropics today. Relying on this similarity, it is estimated that Cro–Magnon was an archaic African race. Some other paleoanthropological finds have shown that the Cro–Magnon and the Neanderthal races intermixed and laid the foundations for the races of our day.

As a result, none of these human beings were "primitive species." They were different human beings who lived in earlier times and either assimilated and mixed with other races, or became extinct and disappeared from history.

It is definite that this race lived together with modern humans, at the same time and in the same areas. The findings testify that Neanderthals buried their dead, fashioned musical instruments, and had cultural affinities with the *H. sapiens sapiens* living during the same period. Entirely modern skulls and skeletal structures of Neanderthal fossils are not open to any speculation. A prominent authority on the subject, Erik Trinkaus from New Mexico University, writes:

"Detailed comparisons of Neanderthal skeletal remains with those of modern humans have shown that there is nothing in Neanderthal anatomy that conclusively indicates locomotor, manipulative, intellectual, or linguistic abilities inferior to those of modern humans."[154]

In fact, Neanderthals even had some "evolutionary" advantages over modern men. The cranial capacity of Neanderthals was larger than that of the modern man and they were more robust and muscular than we are. Trinkaus adds: "One of the most characteristic features of the Neanderthals is the exaggerated massiveness of their trunk and limb bones. All of the preserved bones suggest a strength seldom attained by modern humans. Furthermore, not only is this robustness present among the adult males, as one might expect, but it is also evident in the adult females, adolescents, and even children."

To put it precisely, Neanderthals are a human race that assimilated with other races in time. All of these factors show that the scenario of "human evolution" fabricated by evolutionists is a figment of their imaginations, and that men have always been men and apes always apes.

---

154. Trinkaus, Eric, *Hard Times, Among the Neanderthals Natural History,* No. 87, December 1978, p. 10.

CHAPTER 15

THE HIDDEN HISTORY OF HOMO SAPIENS

The most interesting and significant fact that nullifies the very basis of the imaginary family tree of evolutionary theory is the unexpectedly ancient history of modern man. Paleoanthropological findings reveal that *H. sapiens* were living as long as 1 million years ago according to the evolutionary time scale. It was Louis Leakey, the famous paleoanthropologist, who discovered the first findings on this subject. In 1932, in the Kanjera region around Lake Victoria in Kenya, Leakey found several fossils that belonged to the Middle Pleistocene and that were no different from modern man. However, the Middle Pleistocene was a million years ago.[155] Since these discoveries turned the evolutionary family tree upside down, they were dismissed by some evolutionist paleoanthropologists. Yet Leakey always contended that his estimates were correct.

Just when this controversy was about to be forgotten, a fossil unearthed in Spain in 1995 revealed in a very remarkable way that the history of *H. sapiens* was much older than had been assumed. The fossil in question was uncovered in a cave called Gran Dolina in the Atapuerca region of Spain by three Spanish paleoanthropologists from the University of Madrid. The fossil revealed the face of an 11-year-old boy who looked entirely like modern man. Yet, it had

---

155. Leakey, S. B., *The Origin of Homo Sapiens,* ed. F. Borde, Paris: UNESCO, 1972, p. 25–29; L. S. B. Leakey, *By the Evidence,* New York: Harcourt Brace Jovanovich, 1974.

been 800,000 years since the child died. *Discover* magazine covered the story in great detail in its December 1997 issue.

This fossil even shook the convictions of Juan Luis Arsuaga Ferreras, who lead the Gran Dolina excavation. Ferreras said:

> We expected something big, something large, something inflated—you know, something primitive. Our expectation of an 800,000-year-old boy was something like Turkana boy. And what we found was a totally modern face. . . . To me this is most spectacular—these are the kinds of things that shake you. Finding something totally unexpected like that. Not finding fossils; finding fossils is unexpected too, and it's okay. But the most spectacular thing is finding something you thought belonged to the present, in the past. It's like finding something like—like a tape recorder in Gran Dolina. That would be very surprising. We don't expect cassettes and tape recorders in the Lower Pleistocene. Finding a modern face 800,000 years ago–it's the same thing. We were very surprised when we saw it.[156]

The fossil highlighted the fact that the history of *H. sapiens* had to be extended back to 800,000 years ago. After recovering from the initial shock, the evolutionists who discovered the fossil decided that it belonged to a different species, because according to the evolutionary family tree, *H. sapiens* did not live 800,000 years ago. Therefore, they made up an imaginary species called *"Homo antecessor"* and included the Atapuerca skull under this classification.

There have been many findings demonstrating that *H. sapiens* date back even earlier than 800,000 years. One of them is a discovery by Louis Leakey in the early 1970s in Olduvai Gorge. Here, in the Bed II layer, Leakey discovered that *Australopithecus, H. habilis* and *H. erectus* species had coexisted at the same time. What is even more interesting was a structure Leakey found in the same layer (Bed II). Here, he found the remains of a stone hut. The unusual aspect of the event was that this construction, which is still used in some parts

---

156. "Is This the Face of Our Past," *Discover,* December 1997, pp. 97–100.

of Africa, could only have been built by *H. sapiens!* So, according to Leakey's findings, *Australopithecus, H. habilis, H. erectus* and modern man must have coexisted approximately 1.7 million years ago.[157] This discovery must surely invalidate the evolutionary theory that claims that modern men evolved from apelike species such as *Australopithecus.*

WHAT IT ALL MEANS

What we have investigated so far forms a clear picture: The scenario of "human evolution" is complete fiction. In order for such a family tree to represent the truth, a gradual evolution from ape to man must have taken place and a fossil record of this process should be able to be found. However, there is a huge hole between apes and humans. Skeletal structures, cranial capacities, and such criteria as walking upright or bent sharply forward distinguish humans from apes.[158]

All the evidence from bones and fossils gives only one report: Mankind did not evolve from any lower form of life. Evolutionists have found no support anywhere for their theory that man came from apes, monkeys, mollusks, germs, or anything else. Here are the supposed Ages of Man:

» **Eolithic Age** *(Dawn Stone Age)*—"Animalistic culture, hand-to-mouth eating habits, etc., using natural stone." Date: 3 million years ago.

» **Paleolithic Age** *(Old Stone Age)*—"Savagery culture, food-collecting habits, etc., using chipped stone." Date: 1 million years ago.

Based on carbon–14 dating of organic materials found near metal artifacts:

---

157. Kelso, A. J., *Physical Antropology,* 1st ed., New York: J. B. Lipincott Co., 1970, p. 221; M. D. Leakey, *Olduvai Gorge,* Vol 3, Cambridge: Cambridge University Press, 1971, p. 272.

158. It is interesting to note that research done in 1994 on the inner ear; *Australopithecus* and *H. habilis* were reclassified as apes, while *H. erectus* was reclassified as a fully modern human.

» **Mesolithic Age** *(Middle Stone Age)*—"Barbarism, incipient agriculture, using wood–stone composite materials." Date: 15,000 years ago.

» **Neolithic Age** *(New Stone Age)*—"Civilization, village economy, using polished stone." Date: 9,000 years ago.

» **Copper Age**—"Urbanization, organized state, using polished stone." Date: 7,500 years ago.

» **Bronze Age**—"Urbanization, organized state, using metal." Date: 7,000 years ago.

» **Iron Age**—"Urbanization, organized state, using metal." Date: 5,000 years ago.

It is of interest that all of these living patterns can be found today. Many groups using Dawn, Middle, or New Stone Age methods and materials can be found in New Guinea, southern Philippines, and other primitive areas.

Here are five reasons why mankind did not descend from apes.

1. Abrupt appearance of fossil forms separated by systematic gaps between fossil forms.
2. Distinctness of DNA, chemical components, and pattern (design) of morphological similarities.
3. Laws of Mendel: combination, recombination always results in easily recognized plant, animal forms; *conclusive* evidence of fixed reproductive patterns (designs).
4. Distinctness of human self–conscious awareness, and metaphysical concerns.
5. Distinctness of human personality involving moral and ethical concern; reflective, symbolic, abstract, conceptual thought."[159]

Anthropologists maintain that man descended from an unknown ancestor, and Darwin said it was an ape. If we descended from an ape, why do we have a different number of vertebrae in our backbones

159. Moore, John N., "Teaching about Origin Questions: Origin of Human Beings," *Creation Research Society Quarterly,* March 1986, p. 184.

than apes have? Why is our cranial capacity totally different? And, most important, why is our DNA distinctly different from apes, monkeys, and all species of wildlife?

They say that they have found the bones of our hominid ancestors. Why then have only a table–top full of bones been found? There ought to be millions of bones if they lived for hundreds of thousands of years before us. And why do all those bones look like only ape bones or human bones—and never like both?

They say that modern evolutionary anthropology is based on the pioneering discoveries of six men: Eugene Dubois and his Java man; Charles Dawson's Piltdown man; the 1921 Rhodesian man; the 1922 Nebraska man; Raymond Dart's Taung African man; and Davidson Black's Peking man. But the finds of Dubois and Dawson were later discovered to be outright fakes. Rhodesian and Taung man were found to be apes. Nebraska man turned out to be a pig tooth, and Peking man was just human bones.

Even Richard Leakey, the foremost hominid bone hunter of the past twenty years has begun to question what it is all about. When asked on television to name our ancestor, he walked over to a chalkboard and drew a large question mark. "By 1989, [Richard] Leakey sought to distance himself from his original theory, insisting any attempts at specific reconstructions of the human lineage were premature" (Milner, 1990, p. 218).

Brain size points to the conclusion that most of the skulls are those of apes, while a few are actually people. British anatomist Sir Arthur Keith refused to accept the African *australopithecine* fossils as human ancestors because their brains were too small. Human qualities of mind, Keith proclaimed, can only appear when brain volume is at least 750 cubic centimeters, a point nicknamed *"Keith's rubicon"* (dividing line). And at 450cc, *Australopithecus africanus* didn't qualify.

"In Keith's day, the *Homo erectus* skulls at 950cc could comfortably be included as humans, since their range overlaps our own species (1,000cc–2,000cc). But the *Homo habilis* skulls discovered later measured about 640cc just on the other side of the Rubicon. Skulls of *Australopithecus* adults are about 500cc which is larger than chimps but smaller than *Homo habilis*" (Milner, 1990, p. 249).

Yet another problem—and a highly significant one—concerns the fact that immature apes have skulls which are like those of human beings.

"Adult chimps and gorillas, for instance, have elongated faces, heavy brow ridges, powerful jaws, small braincase in relation to overall skull and other characteristic proportions. Baby apes have flat faces, rounded braincase, light brow ridges, proportionately smaller jaws, and many other bodily features strikingly like human beings" (Milner, 1990, p. 325).

The full implication of this point is of the highest significance; yet it has been acknowledged by few evolutionist anthropologists. *Consider these three facts:* (1) It is well-known that many extinct animals were gigantic in size. (2) Young apes have skulls which are shaped similarly to those of humans. (3) Relics of what once was an amazingly large ape have been found. Put together those facts, and what do you have? The possibility that anthropologists today could come across skulls which are shaped much like those of human beings, yet with small braincases (in the 400–900cc range), which are actually immature giant apes!

[A giant ape lived] during the mid–Pleistocene, about 300,000 years ago. This massive primate probably stood nine feet tall and weighed about 600 pounds, if the rest of the creature was in scale with its teeth and jaws. It was named *Gigantopithecus* (gigantic ape) because its jawbone and teeth are five times larger than that of modern man.

In 1935, remains of *Gigantopthecus* were accidentally discovered in a Hong Kong pharmacy by G. H. R. von Koenigswald, a Dutch paleontologist. Chinese apothecaries have always stocked unusual fossils, which they call "dragon's teeth," for use in ground-up medicines. Von Koenigswald regularly searched these drug-stores for curiosities and was amazed to find an enormous tooth with an apelike (Y–5) dental pattern. When more teeth began to show up, a field search began, which has since yielded hundreds of *Gigantopithecus* teeth and jawbones from various sites in China and Pakistan; other parts of the skeleton, however, have not yet been found.

There are tantalizing reports that bones of the two species [giant ape and human beings] are mingled at the site [in north Vietnam where research scientists are now finding *Gigantopithecus* bones].

—Milner, 1990, p. 192

The search for hominid skulls usually occurs in areas well able to preserve skulls of both apes and men for thousands of years. But relatively few have been found, simply because time only goes back a few thousand years. Some of those skulls could be immature giant apes. These would appear to be small–brained creatures that are quite similar to humans, yet bear a number of differences.

CHAPTER 16

FOOTPRINTS: THE HUMAN DIMENSION

WHY ARE FOSSIL FOOTPRINTS IMPORTANT?

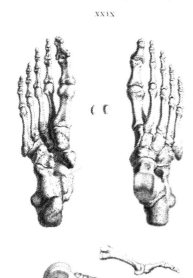

Ichnology is the branch of biology that deals with traces of an organism's behavior. It is generally considered as a branch of paleontology. However, only one division of ichnology, paleoichnology, deals with trace fossils. Fossilized tracks are trace fossils, and fossilized footprints are useful in revealing information about the morphology of the foot.

Anatomically, the human foot is of the plantigrade form. The bottom of the foot is called the sole and the area just behind the toes is called the ball. The skin at the sole of the foot is denser than any other skin on the human body. The density of the sole of the foot has not increased as evolutionary theory postulates. Nor is there one anatomical change found in the fossil footprints that can prove the evolution of man. The foot is a postural structure, meaning it cannot undergo any change that would not affect every part of the body that relates to posture at the same time! This devastates the evolutionary concept that man evolved over long ages.

The foot consists of the (1) ankle, (2) heel bone, (3) instep, (4) metatarsus, and (5) the toes. The human foot combines mechanical complexity and structural strength. The foot and ankle contain 26 bones, 33 joints, and more than 100 muscles, tendons, and ligaments. The major bones in the human foot are:

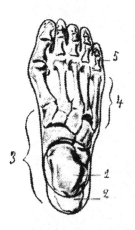

>> *Phalanges*: The bones in the toes
>> *Metatarsals*: The bones in the middle of the foot
>> *Cuneiforms*: Three bones in the middle of the foot, toward the center of the body
>> *Cuboid*: The bone sitting adjacent to the cuneiforms on the outside of the foot
>> *Navicular*: sits behind the cuneiforms
>> *Talus*: Also called the ankle bone, the talus sits directly behind the navicular.
>> *Calcaneus*: Also called the heel bone; the largest bone in the foot.

The ankle serves as foundation, shock absorber, and propulsion. The foot can sustain enormous pressure and provides flexibility and resiliency. Structurally, the forefoot bears half the body's weight and balances pressure on the ball of the foot. The mid–foot has five irregularly shaped tarsal bones, forms the foot's arch, and serves as a shock absorber. The bones of the mid–foot are connected to the forefoot and the hind–foot by muscles and the plantar fascia (arch ligament). These components work together to provide the body with support, balance, and mobility.

BIPEDALISM

Bipedalism is considered a defining event in human evolution. According to scientists, there are at least twelve distinct hypotheses about bipedalism. Bipedalism is a characteristic only of human beings and this quality is the most distinctive factor that distinguishes human beings from other animals. A human's hips, pelvis, backbone, in fact, all parts of his skeleton, are designed for bipedalism.

Therefore, while interpreting the uncovered fossils, the most important and binding criteria should be bipedalism. Bipedalism is the most substantial factor that distinguishes humans from apes.

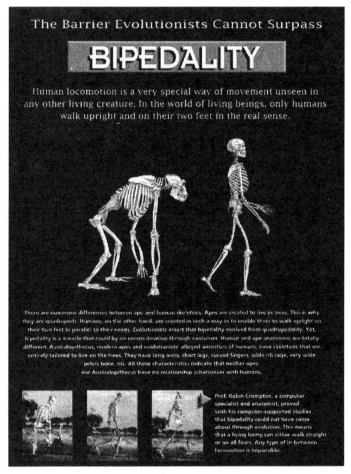

The human skeleton is designed to walk upright. Ape skeletons, however, with their forward-leaning stance, short legs, and long arms, are suited to walking on four legs. It is not possible for there to be an intermediate form" between them, because this would be extremely unproductive.

This is why the focal point of arguments must consist of whether the living things at issue walk upright or not.

Apart from the fossil record we have dealt with so far, unbridgeable anatomical gaps between men and apes also invalidate the fiction of human evolution. One of these has to do with the manner of walking.

Human beings walk upright on two feet. The placement of the large toe in humans is unique. In *pongids*, such as the gorilla, the big toe is positioned so that it can be used in climbing and grasping. The big toe in pongids is used in a manner similar to the thumb. In humans the big toe is parallel with the other toes, important for walking bipedally. The human heel is four times the size of a gorilla heel and twice that of a chimpanzee. This is because it contains a lot of spongy bone that absorbs the shock of walking. This is a very special form of locomotion not seen in any other mammalian species. While some other animals do have a limited ability to move when they stand on their two hind feet, animals like bears and monkeys, they can move in this way only rarely, such as when they want to reach a source of food, and then only for a short time. Normally, their skeletons lean forward and they walk on all fours.

So, has bipedalism then evolved from the quadrupedal gait of apes as evolutionists claim? Of course not. Research has shown that the evolution of bipedalism never occurred, nor is it possible for it to have done so. First of all, bipedalism is not an evolutionary advantage. The way in which apes move is much easier, faster, and more efficient than man's bipedal stride. Man can neither move by jumping from tree to tree like a chimpanzee, nor run like a cheetah. On the contrary, since man walks on two feet, he moves much more slowly on the ground. For the same reason, he is one of the most unprotected of all species in nature in terms of movement and defense. According to the logic of evolution, apes should not have evolved to adopt a bipedal stride; instead, humans should have evolved to become quadrupedal.

What really embarrassed evolutionists was the discovery that *Australopithecus* could not have walked on two feet with a bent posture. It would have been physically very ineffective for *Australopithe-*

cus to move about in such a way because of the enormous energy demands it would have entailed. Another impasse of the evolutionary claim is that bipedalism does not serve the gradual development model of Darwinism. This model, which constitutes the basis of evolution, requires that there should be a "compound" stride between bipedalism and quadrupedalism.

However, with the computerized research he conducted in 1996, Robin Crompton, senior lecturer in anatomy at Liverpool University, showed that such a compound stride was not possible. Crompton reached the following conclusion: A living being can either walk upright, or on all fours; they cannot do both. A type of in-between stride cannot be sustained for long periods because of the extreme energy consumption. Therefore, *Australopithecus* could not have been both bipedal and have a bent walking posture. A half-bipedal being cannot exist. *Australopithecus* is an ordinary ape that strolls on all fours.

Animals named as *australopithecines* are introduced by the evolutionists as living beings that are able to stand on their two feet but possess underdeveloped brains and skeletons. Although some of these scientists admit that *Australopithecus* are similar to apes in many primitive aspects, they advance a very important argument relating it to a human: They claim that *Australopithecus* walked like today's human beings. On the contrary, the latest scientific researches indicate that *Australopithecus*, which was found in 1920s, was definitely not bipedal.

According to *LiveScience*:

A re-examination of anklebones from early hominids indicates their gait was not as stable as previous research suggested. Their feet were thought to be very much like ours, suggesting they had mastered bipedalism. "We noticed that in the specimens of robust *australopithecines*, there were characteristics of the anklebone that would have affected its bipedal locomotion," said Gary Schwartz, an Arizona State University anthropologist. "By looking at the location where the shin bone rides across the anklebone, we found that the shin bones would have been angled inward. . . .

The skeletal modifications associated with bipedalism represent a phenomenal reorganization of one's anatomy," Schwartz said. "It is unlikely that it could have evolved independently in multiple hominin lineages."[160]

Scientists keep trying to come up with ways that bipedalism could have occurred. Now they say that bipedalism may have occurred in the trees some 21 million years ago according to another *LiveScience* article.[161]

> . . . The earliest upright ape known so far was the extinct hominoid, *Morotopithecus bishopi*, which lived in Uganda more than 21 million years ago. A strange birth defect in what may have been the first direct human ancestor led this septum to cross behind the spinal cord in the lumbar or lower back region—an odd configuration more typical of invertebrates. This would have made horizontal stances inefficient. In other words, "the other great apes we see now, such as chimps or gorillas or orangutans, might have descended from humanlike ancestors," said researcher Aaron Filler, a Harvard-trained evolutionary biologist and medical director at Cedars-Sinai Institute for Spinal Disorders in Los Angeles. If bipedalism did evolve 21 million years ago, "it more likely evolved to walk in trees than on the ground," said University of Chicago evolutionary anthropologist Russell Tuttle. "Twenty-one million years ago, there were a lot of trees around," he said.

Yet again in *LiveScience* scientists just skip the necessity of learning how our "ancestors" first walked by suggesting that "*Human Ancestors May Have Hit the Ground Running.*"[162] Now if you believe all this

---

160. Britt, Robert Roy, "Ancient Human Ancestors were Knock-kneed," LiveScience Managing Editor, posted: 16 February 2006 at http://www.livescience.com/health/060216_human_walk.html.

161. Choi, Charles Q., "Human Ancestors Walked Upright, Study Claims," Special to LiveScience, posted: 09 October 2007 at http://www.livescience.com/strangenews/071009-upright-early.html.

162. Choi, Charles Q., "Human Ancestors May Have Hit the Ground Run-

wishy–washy back and forth nonsense, believe me, they have more baloney for sale than your local grocer does! Simply put, these assertions are wrong.

Charles Oxnard, an anatomy professor from Chicago University, is one of the most consulted evolutionists who is shown as reference on the subject of *Australopithecus*. Relying on his research about *Australopithecus* fossils, Oxnard declared that these fossils did not belong to a transitional being between apes and men, and therefore did not have a kinship with human beings.

An important part of today's conventional wisdom about human evolution is based on studies of teeth, jaws, and skull fragments of *australopithecine* fossils. These all indicate that the close relation of *australopithecine* to the human lineage may not be true. All these fossils are both different than gorillas, chimpanzees, and men. Studying as a group, *australopithecine* seems more like to the orangutan. Oxnard also stated that this species could only walk on all fours:

> But because the muscular features of the pelvis are positioned in a way more like those of the great apes, we must estimate that their muscular arrangements were therefore rather similar to those associated with climbing and perhaps quadrupedalism . . . which parallels most closely the orangutan, and contrasts markedly with man who has big articular surfaces in the leg compared with the arm. They may have been bipedal in a way that is no longer seen, but have retained abilities for climbing, and perhaps minor arboreal acrobatics such as might be found in an intermediately sized apelike creature.

Dean Falk, a brain specialist who has conducted more recent research on four different types of *Australopithecus* fossils said that these were nothing but apes. Since 1985, many more apelike characteristics of *Australopithecus*es have been found than previously supposed. Opinions regarding Taung and other *Australopithecus*es

ning," Special to LiveScience, posted: 24 July 2006 at http://www.livescience.com/animals/060724_gibbons_walking.html.

have reversed. Studies of young researchers like Bill Jungers, Holly Smith, Tim Bromage, Mike Vannier, and Glenn Conroy are now being questioned. The supporters of the judgment "*Australopithecus* is man-like" are not the majority now. The morphology of *Australopithecuses* is extremely similar to the apes.

Bipedalism should not be credited to *Australopithecus.* But, to give their theory some room for error, evolutionists say that while *Australopithecus* generally walked on two feet, they were also adapted to climbing and using four feet. Yet, it is not possible to walk in this style. In order for a living being to use its energy optimally, it must either walk on four feet or on two feet in an upright posture. It is not possible for a living being to do both and carry on its existence and generation. This is why the bipedal model ascribed to the *Australopithecus* can be said to be complete fantasy.

In his study titled "The Antiquity of Human Walking," John R. Napier compares the walking styles of *Australopithecus* and human beings. ". . . In *Australopithecus* this stabilizing mechanism is imperfectly evolved. . . . These hominids must have covered the ground with quick, rather short steps, with their knees and hips slightly bent; the prolonged stance phase of the fully human gait must surely have been absent. Compared with man's stride, therefore, the gait of *Australopithecus* is physiologically inefficient. It calls for a disproportionately high output of energy; indeed, *Australopithecus* probably found long-distance bipedal travel impossible."

Research done on *Australopithecus* using recent advanced technology demonstrates that these creatures could not walk on their two feet, and verified all the above findings. In 1994, Fred Spoor, an anatomist in England's Liverpool University Human Anatomy and Cell Biology Department, and his team of researchers made bipedalism studies on fossils, investigated if *Australopithecus* were bipedal or not by using the most recent techniques. With these techniques, the team examined the involuntary-balancing mechanism in the ear cochlea of the fossils.

The upright posture and obligatory bipedalism of modern humans are unique among living primates. The evolutionary history of this behavior has traditionally been pursued by functional analysis of the postcranial skeleton and the preserved footprint trails of fossil hominids. Here we report a systematic attempt to reconstruct the locomotor behavior of early hominids by looking at a major component of the mechanism for the unconscious perception of movement, namely by examining the vestibular system of living primates and early hominids. High resolution computed tomography was used to generate cross–sectional images of the bony labyrinthine. In contrast, the semicircular canal dimensions in crania from Southern Africa attributed to *Australopithecus* and *Paranthropus* resemble those of the great apes.

They go on to state that *Australopithecus* and hominid fossils of early *Homo* ages do not show a morphological structure in consort with the structure of the modern man.

As revealed by all these researchers, being just an ordinary ape species that lived in the past, all that *Australopithecus* could do was to stand on their two feet for very short intervals, just like today's gorillas and bulky apes. Actually, the evolutionists who were aiming at finding an ape fossil that could walk on its two feet advanced unreal assertions by making use of lack of information caused by technological scarcity.

Consequently, these improvements resulted in disagreements between paleontologists regarding the direct kinship between *Australopithecus* and human beings. Anybody who examines the given data objectively may easily realize that the body structure of *Australopithecus* is just the same as tailless huge apes still living today. Finding humanlike qualities in these animals can only be possible by a biased point of view and broad imagination.

IS BIPEDALISM AN EVOLUTIONARY ADVANTAGE?

Man's stride is a very special act unprecedented among living beings. We perform this act so easily that we are usually unaware of how complex this act actually is. A more detailed examination of this will make it clearer that the act rests upon extremely sensitive balances.

When the first step is taken, only the coming of the second step can stop man from falling down. When the person wants to take a step, the pelvis bone, the legs, and other parts of the body engage in a series of muscle movements. Gravity forms the energy to withstand the acceleration of the body. When one foot is swung forward, the center of gravity of the body then moves forward. Meanwhile, the other foot touches the ground to provide balance. The pelvis bone plays a very important role in this movement as the rotation angle of the pelvis bone determines how far ahead the foot can go. Also, the muscles on the bone help to maintain the balance of the body when the foot is swung forward.

All the while, the foot behind the body's center of gravity provides the source of energy which moves the body forward. Ground is first pushed by the heel, then by the toe, and energy is produced by the walking person through the usage of the muscles. This is the "pushing" stage of walking. The foot at the back passes over to the starting point of the walking act, that is, the "swinging" stage, as soon as its interaction with the ground is over. As the foot is swung forward, it does not hit the ground because the knee, ankle, and pelvis are slightly bent. The acceleration is slowed down due to the slightly high pose of the foot while it is swung forward.

Before the foot swung ahead steps on the ground, the knee flattens but the ankle remains bent. Hence, the heel touches on the ground first. With the stepping of the heel on the ground, the circle is completed and the other foot enters the swinging stage once more.

Ebenhart and his friends made studies during World War II to develop artificial legs. Later widening the scope of their research, they found that the body was moving its center of gravity in space with minimum energy by means of a series of deterministic factors. In man's stride, many factors like gravity, acceleration of the body, and balance, interact with each other in harmony and ensure that minimum energy is spent during the action.

Human stride is such a meticulous balance and precise adjustment that no robot can be made to perform this movement despite the time consuming trials on the subject. The robots which are manufactured adopting man's stride lose their balance and fall down as soon as they lift up their foot to take a step due to hopeless failure in the adjustment of the center of gravity.

In an experiment designed to overcome this negative effect, a relatively big pendulum was placed at the back of the robot, and was adjusted to sway in the opposite direction of the foot that was lifted to take a step. The limping/walking style attained through this method could only be carried on at a constant speed. The movement ability of man, who can change his speed as he likes, cannot be imitated at all despite all efforts.

The most interesting point is that human beings never have to plan or think how they are going to walk. Man accomplishes a difficult movement unconsciously, as if it had to happen anyway. The act of walking is a quite complex action that is performed by the *peripheral nervous system,* which consists of the *somatic* and *autonomic* nervous systems. The somatic nervous system is responsible for controlling voluntary movements during activities such as walking.

This raises a very important question. How did the "hominids" evolve such intricate nervous systems and spinal structures? How did they happen to acquire such ability during the evolutionary process? Did they think it into existence? Hold on a second. I think I have a great answer to fix such a problem. It was a genetic mutation that resulted in more complexity in order for the "hominid" to produce *more work* in order to be *more efficient for survival.* Really? So when did mutations constitute new information? Isn't mutation the *loss of information?* And when is it ever beneficial? Is there not a harmful side effect to a mutation?

Subsequently, the second law of thermodynamics gets put on hold while an *increase* in information operates in reverse to conveniently accommodate the evolutionary model. How suitable. And what happened to survival of the fittest? If hominids were not initially equipped to walk upright then, according to evolution, they should have been phased out altogether. Isn't it more difficult to learn to stand erect if you're used to climbing around like an ape? Think how hard it is to get up in the mornings sometimes. The easy action to take is to lie back down. You conserve energy this way. The difficult task is standing up and walking because it involves work. You see, it isn't really rocket science. You just need to think like an evolutionist to get an answer to fit their theory. It goes without saying that the evolutionists have no real answer to this question at all.

The evolutionary theories regarding the root causes of bipedalism rest upon speculation. Evolutionists face a big problem because, when examined in terms of mechanics, it is seen that quadrupedalism is superior to bipedalism. A living being able to move on all fours can run faster and has more chance to survive. Bipedal stride is both harder and slower. Therefore, a thesis claiming that bipedalism evolved out of quadrupedalism cannot be explained by natural selection, which is based on the argument of survival of the fittest.

If we think in terms of evolutionary criteria, we have to contend that the bipedal stride of man is more advanced and successful than the quadrupedal ape. Yet, it cannot be said that contemporary apes are unsuccessful in terms of evolution, because they possess the characteristics most fitting to their environment and they have the ability to move in the most appropriate way for themselves.

Niles Eldredge states with a question that the idea of "improvement of creatures through evolution" is logically untrue. Do plant and animal species really improve and develop into a more complex structure? If this is the case, then should we consider the simple and unchanged life forms, such as the sponge, as evolutionary failures? The evolutionary slogan "the evolutional is inevitable" should be replaced with "why apes are successful."

The theory of evolution is absolutely paradoxical about this subject. According to the theory, transition from ape to man (hence from ape's stride to man's stride) should be considered to be an improvement. However, the ape's stride is easier, faster, and more efficient when compared to man's stride. Human beings can neither proceed by jumping from tree to tree like chimpanzees nor run like a cheetah. On the contrary, man moves in a much slower fashion on the ground due to its bipedal stride. Again for the same reason, he is one of the most defenseless creatures in nature in terms of movement and protection.

If we admit the evolutionary argument, we must assent to the idea that man's first ancestor split off from the apes and started to walk on its two feet in an upright posture. But, since bipedalism is a disadvantage rather than an advantage, natural selection would eliminate this ancestor of man. This is one of the biggest contradictions within evolution itself.

EXPLANATIONS BY EVOLUTIONISTS

Evolutionists are far from bringing a logical explanation to the emergence of bipedalism. Their interpretations on the subject do not depend on any concrete facts, but rather on speculations produced out of their imagination. It can even be observed that sometimes these speculations are covered up with an ideological and emotional disguise.

Ilhan Selçuk declared that the first ape that was supposed to have stood on its two feet was a leftist and set a very good example for the emotional nature of the evolutionists. "Donald C. Johnson named the first human passing from horizontal position to the vertical as *Australopithecus afarensis;* later on, this man who stood on his feet for the first time was called 'Lucy.' Which innate instinct and external effect caused man to stand on his feet while he was walking like an animal? Why had he diverged from the majority while

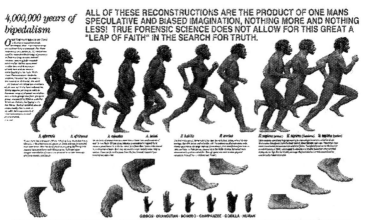

4,000,000 years of bipedalism

ALL OF THESE RECONSTRUCTIONS ARE THE PRODUCT OF ONE MANS SPECULATIVE AND BIASED IMAGINATION, NOTHING MORE AND NOTHING LESS! TRUE FORENSIC SCIENCE DOES NOT ALLOW FOR THIS GREAT A "LEAP OF FAITH" IN THE SEARCH FOR TRUTH.

THE INTERESTING THING ABOUT THE FEET IS THAT ALL OF THEM ARE CLEARLY HOMO SAPIEN FEET. THIS CONJECTURE IS DUE TO THE FACT THAT ALL OF THE FOOT PRINTS FOUND IN THE FOSSIL RECORD TO DATE ARE ANATOMICALLY IDENTICAL WITH MODERN MAN. WHETHER ATTRIBUTED TO AUSTRALOPITHECUS AFARENSIS (LUCY)-NEANDERTHAL, THEY ARE INDISTINGUISHABLE FROM MODERN MAN. THERE ARE NO APE, CHIMPANZEE OR MONKEY FOOT PRINTS AND, PERPLEXING FOR EVOLUTIONISTS, THERE ARE NO FOOT PRINTS CLEARLY REPRESENTING "MONKEY TO MAN TRANSITIONAL FOOT PRINTS" OF ANY KIND IN THE FOSSIL RECORD, PERIOD!
THERE IS A SIMPLE REASON FOR THIS. MAN HAS ALWAYS BEEN MAN, NOTHING MORE AND NOTHING LESS!

walking on all fours? Wasn't this man who stood up for the first time making a revolution? Maybe, this man standing up was the first 'leftist.' . . ."

Other theories on the root causes of bipedalism, seemingly more scientific, actually consist of groundless speculations and interpretations. Evolutionary arguments of both Darwin's era and modern times rest upon these baseless speculations. Since the sciences of genetics and hereditary laws were not very well known in the nineteenth century, explaining bipedalism seemed easy for Darwin and his followers. The most popular theory was that the apes living in the savannas of Africa stretched their necks in order to look over the high bushes and thus bipedalism originated. It did not take long to understand that the Lamarckism theory was entirely incorrect.

Contemporary evolutionists assert only a single thesis regarding the origins of bipedalism. When examined closer, it is possible to see that this theory, the best of the worst, is far from an explanation on the origins of bipedalism, just like the previous ones. According to the "theory of transition from woods to the open field," the common ancestors of men and apes used to live together in the woods. With the reduction of woodlands and possibly other reasons, some of them passed over to the open fields, which gave way to bipedalism as a result of adaptation. Thus, the roads of the apes in the trees and bipedal men living in the fields separated, and both started to carry on with their evolution in their own direction.

Although this theory of transition from woods to the open field receives a lot of support, it is extremely baseless, primarily because this kind of an adaptation is impossible on a molecular level. Even if it is presumed to have occurred, there is no evidence of it in the fossil records. Furthermore, according to this theory, woodlands in East Africa should have started to diminish, yet the studies have proved just the opposite and disclosed that East Africa did not undergo such a change. Studies conducted by J. D. Kingston in Kenya in 1995 reveal concrete evidence to prove this theory wrong. Kingston writes: "Analyses of the stable carbon isotopic composition {$d13\ C$} of paleosol carbonate and organic matter from the Tugen Hills succession in Kenya indicate that a heterogeneous environment with a mix of

C3 and C4 plants has persisted for the last 15.5 million years. Open grasslands at no time dominated this portion of the rift valley. The observed d13 C values offer no evidence for a shift to more–closed C3 environments to C4 grassland habitats. If hominids evolved in East Africa during the Late Miocene, they did so in an ecologically diverse setting."

Briefly, the transition from woodlands to savanna in East Africa is never realized. The plantation in this region remains the same for millions of years.

Even if assessed logically, the theory on the roots of bipedalism is unacceptable. It is asserted that the shrinking of woods urged the apes to travel to the open fields and transfer to bipedal stride. How rational is this idea? In our day, do the shrinking woods lead some apes to descend from the trees and adapt to the ground environment? Is it possible that these apes started using tools after descending from the trees and becoming bipedal? Are these quadrupedal apes going to be bipedal by means of a magical stick?

There is no doubt that the answer to these questions will be negative. In the case of declining trees, the most natural behavior of the apes would be migrating to another region, or else these apes would die out as a result of the destruction of their homelands. There is no basis for the theory claiming that the apes came down from the trees and adapted to the conditions on the ground.

There are many questions besides the question of "why the apes could not succeed" and all of these still remain unanswered.

Elaine Morgan, an evolutionary paleoanthropologist, makes the following confession in relation to this matter: Four of the most outstanding mysteries about humans are: 1) Why do they walk on two legs? 2) Why have they lost their fur? 3) Why have they developed such large brains? 4) Why did they learn to speak?

The traditional answers to these questions are: 1. "We don't know"; 2. "We don't know"; 3. "We don't know"; 4. "We don't know."

And they will never know.

CHAPTER 17

TRACKING HUMANS
A TESTIMONY IN THE ROCKS

Human footprints have been found in ancient rock strata. Evolution says that man did not evolve until the late Tertiary, and therefore cannot be more than 1 to 3 million years old. Modern men and women are supposed to have existed on this Earth for only the past 2 million years, whereas the great majority of the sedimentary strata are supposed to extend from 25 million to 570 million years in the past. But there are evidences that people were alive at the time when those strata were laid down. This would either mean that people are billions of years old or that the strata are quite young. The evidence clearly shows that these footprints were made when the rocks were soft mud. Either modern man lived in the very earliest evolutionary eras of prehistory, or all rock dating must be shrunk down to a much shorter time frame—during all of which man lived.

But could these supposed ancient rock strata contain fossilized modern human footprints? To the scientific community it's unthinkable and unacceptable. Why? Because they would have to conclude that either modern man is much older than we have thought or that our dating techniques are faulty. Either way, there is a big problem for scientists.

Science seeks to answer the provocative question about life's origins. Did we evolve over millions of years through environmental pressures and mutations? Were our ancestors alienlike creatures from outer space, with advanced genetics and technology that seeded our race? Or are we the product of special creation as outlined in Genesis?

Trackways and footprints can be analyzed to understand how people moved, what their environment was like, how fast they were, and behavioral patterns of their culture. The study of fossil human footprints has become more popular in the last twenty years as scientists recognized the importance of these ancient traces. Other revelations include the size of the person and what kind of material they were moving around on. This is one of the characteristics of fossil footprints that make them helpful in analyzing their history. These footprints stamped in time help solve this ancient mystery. When a depression that resembles a footprint is found, there are four possibilities it can be:

1. A footprint
2. A natural formation
3. A carved human footprint or fake
4. Animal footprint, which has been altered geologically to appear human

Because there is much ground to cover on the tracks around the world, let's take a look at the most controversial track site in the world, the Paluxy riverbed in Glen Rose, Texas. Since there has been much evidence that has been documented in the last 30 years on the Paluxy, I will only present the most recent evidence here.

Texas
Valley of the Giants
Next to Laetoli, probably the most publicized human fossil footprints are those found along the Paluxy River, near Glen Rose, Texas. Glen Rose is noted for its rich history of early settlers and the natural artesian water that flowed freely from the ground. One of the worst flash floods recorded put Glen Rose into the history books. In 1908, the Paluxy River rose an astounding 27 feet. Little did residents of this small town realize what had been lurking underneath the limestone layers of the Paluxy. As the water receded, mysterious three–

toed tracks appeared!

Young George Adams, brother of Earnest "Bull" Adams, is credited with discovering the tracks in 1908. They were originally thought to be giant turkey tracks, and therefore of no significant importance. George Adams reported his findings to his local high school teacher, Robert E. McDonald, who identified them as belonging to dinosaurs. They would later be recognized as theropod tracks, those of a carnivorous dinosaur. In 1932, Charlie Moss of Glen Rose discovered the first known sauropod tracks, known then as brontosaur tracks. However, it wasn't until Roland T. Bird, paleontologist for the American Museum of Natural History in New York, visited the area in the fall of 1938 that Glen Rose was put on the paleontological map. Eventually, his findings were brought to national attention in 1954 with an article featured in *National Geographic* magazine.

Glen Rose is located in north central Texas, about 40 miles southwest of the Dallas–Fort Worth metropolitan area. The area has little rainfall and for several months each year the Paluxy River is completely dry. From time to time, the river changes its course. This occurs at those times when the quiet river becomes a raging torrent. Because the river has such a steep slope (a drop of seven feet per mile), it is the second–swiftest river in Texas and quite dangerous in times of heavy rainfall.

The flash flood in 1908 washed away a portion of shore ledge, exposing the footprints in cretaceous stone. The so–called *Cretaceous period* is the only time when the dinosaurs were supposed to have lived. This period is thought to have spanned 65 million years over the course of history. Man is thought to have appeared no earlier than 3 million years ago. The "Glen Rose formation," as it is known by geologists, is dated as Early Cretaceous, or 120 million years ago. This formation is composed of limestone, alternating with clay, marl, and sand, and is various shades of brownish yellow and gray. Its thickness is 40 to 200 feet. Preservation of such tracks in *limestone* provides conclusive proof of rapid formation.

As soon as the tracks were made, a layer of clay, sand, and gravel washed in and filled them so they would not dissolve away. The prints were covered and preserved fast! If the tracks had not been quickly covered, they would have eroded away. There is no room here for hundreds or millions of years. Today, when tracks are exposed, they erode quickly due to exposure to the elements. It may well be that the prints were covered by rising, turbulent water, which, after covering them with sediments, moved away temporarily as the Earth may have moved up or down. It was a time of geologic catastrophe on a massive scale.

It was not until the 1930s that Clifford L. Burdick, a mining geologist, and Roland T. Bird, a paleontologist with the American Museum of Natural History in New York, carefully examined and reported on the footprints. In 1938, Roland Bird removed a significantly long trail of dinosaur tracks that were then transported to the American Museum of Natural History back in New York City. C. L. Burdick's findings were published in the 1957 issue of *The Naturalist.*

However, Bird was not only intrigued with the dinosaur tracks but with the human footprints that he found on the Paluxy as well. Bird commented, "Yes, they apparently are real enough. Real as the rock could be ... the strangest things of their kind I had ever seen. On the surface of each was splayed the near–likeness of a human foot, perfect in every detail. But each imprint was 15 inches long."[163]

Another genuine piece of evidence about these footprints is the "mud push–up" they display. Mud push–up is where the toes push up the mud in front and on the sides. This would not occur if these were erosion markings, as some evolutionists claim. "Lamination markings," indicating that the foot pressed through different colored clays beneath it, are also to be seen on many of the human and animal tracks. Over 100 human footprint trails have been studied in the Paluxy River area alone.

Subsequently, many others began to investigate the footprints as well, people such as Berney Neufeld,[164] Fred Beierle,[165] and Dr.

---

163. Bird, Roland T., "Thunder in His Footsteps," *Natural History,* May 1939, p. 255.
164. Neufeld, Berney, 1975, "Dinosaur Tracks and Giant Men", *Origins,* Vol. 2, No. 2.
165. Beierle, Fred, 1977, *Man, Dinosaurs, and History,* Prosser, WA: Perfect Printing Co.

Wilder-Smith.[166] C. N. Dougherty, a local chiropractor in the Glen Rose area, in 1967 wrote a book, *Valley of the Giants*.[167] He has located, described, and photographed many of the human prints.

THE TAYLOR TRAIL

Stan Taylor (pointing at track) began his excavation of the Taylor Trail in 1969 and continued working through 1972. Initially, only two tracks could be seen in the Paluxy riverbed. By following the trail back under the river bank, seven more very human like tracks were exposed. The process involved removing tons of limestone overburden, effectively eliminating the possibility that the tracks were carved.

Subsequent excavation has extended the trail to a total of 14 tracks in a consistent right-left pattern. The entire sequence can be seen through the water in this 1994 photograph, even though a thin layer of mud obscures the details. A trail of three-toed dinosaur tracks can be seen crossing at an angle of approximately 30 degrees.

166. Wilder-Smith, A., 1968. *Man's Origin, Man's Destiny.* Harold Shaw Co.: Wheaton.
167. Dougherty, Cecil N., 1979 (sixth edition), *Valley of the Giants,* Bennett printing Company, Cleburne, TX.

The drought of 1999 revealed the entire trail in dramatic detail! It was during this time that I helped Joe Taylor of the Mt. Blanco Fossil Museum and the Creation Evidence Museum craft a complete 60-foot latex mold of this trail in situ.

Perhaps the strongest feature of the evidence presented by the Taylor Trail is the fact that it is composed of a sequence of 14 tracks, consistent in length, in a consistent right–left pattern. The largest variance from the average is less than 5 percent. In the sequence of associated dinosaur tracks, length varies as much as 40 percent.

Individual toes can be discerned in seven of the 14 tracks. Such detail is unexpected. In Mary Leakey's Laetoli tracks, one great toe can be distinguished but no individual small toes can be seen.

Left–right distinctions can be made in 12 of the 14 tracks. Two are simply oblong shapes. When such determinations can be made, they are left-right consistent, with lefts where lefts should be and rights where rights should be. Above is a picture of –3B track.

The average distance between the tracks is 2.6 feet. If the individual's proportions were average, a height of 6'4" would be indicated. For such an individual, an average distance between steps of 2.6 feet is completely normal. Actually, the distance begins about 2½ feet and declines. At 3B (a standing track) he appears to stop. The heel of the next print is not as far ahead as the toes of 3B. From that point they begin to lengthen, indicating increasing speed. The greatest distance is between the last prints. With momentum increasing, the longer distance between these tracks is appropriate.

A statistical anomaly is represented in the following chart[168]

No.	Human Shape	Length	Toes	Left/ Right?	L–R Consistent
+6	✓	11"	✓	L	✓
+5	✓	11.5"	✓	R	✓
+4	✓	11.5"	✓	?	✓
+3	✓	11.75"	✓	R	✓
+2	✓	11.75"	0	L	✓
+1	✓	11.75"	✓	R	✓
−1	✓	11.5"	0	L	✓
−2	✓	11.5"	✓	R	✓
−3	✓	11.5"	0	L	✓
−3B	✓	11"	✓	R	✓
−3C	✓	11.75"	?	L	✓
−4	✓	11.75"	0	?	✓
−5	✓	11.5"	?	L	✓
−6	✓	11.75"	0	R	✓
14	14	Av.11.53	7	12	14

Later, the documentary film *Footprints in Stone* (1973) was made which featured the discovery on the Paluxy.[169] In the 1980s, John Morris of ICR also took an interest in the tracks and authored an *Impact* article and a book, *Tracking Those Incredible Dinosaurs,* on the subject.[170]

The most remarkable fact of all, however, is that these prints are in the same layer as dinosaur tracks, and, in a few instances, the human and dinosaur prints cross each other, showing that the two had been contemporary when the rock had been mud. The significance of these examples was noted by Dr. A. E. Wilder Smith of the Uni-

168. www.bible.ca/tracks.

169. *Footprints in Stone,* Films for Christ, 1973, Stan Taylor.

170. Morris, J., 1976. *The Paluxy Rivertracks.* Institute for Creation Research: Impact 35. (May); J. Morris, 1980. *Tracking Those incredible dinosaurs.* CLP Publishers: San Diego

versity of Illinois: "One authentic man–track found in the same stratum as one authentic brontosaurus track throws out 100 years of evolutionary teachings. It is sufficient to bring the whole Darwinistic theory down and revolutionize all biology today."[171]

Human footprint excavated within a dinosaur track on the Paluxy River in July 1997. Because the footprints were buried in tons of limestone that was removed in excavation, carving is an impossibility. The footprint and dinosaur print together requires that they be made at the same time as the mud must be solidified quickly in order to preserve the prints.

THE UPPER TAYLOR PLATFORM: THE MCFALL TRAIL

A trail of human fossil footprints in association with dinosaur footprints was discovered by the author and Dr. Don Patton in 1999 in the Paluxy riverbed, near Glen Rose, Texas. This new trail on the Up-

---

171. Wilder–Smith, A., 1968. *Man's Origin, Man's Destiny* (135f, 293f).

per Taylor Platform, called the McFall Trail, begins about 25 meters upstream from the Taylor Trail (excavated in the early '70s) and trends in the same direction, offset a couple of meters to the left. It ends where two "perfect human footprints," according to Emmit McFall, were cut out by him and the Wilson brothers in the 1940s.

Originally, lime mud similar to wet concrete washed over dinosaur tracks and filled them. After the dinosaur tracks were filled, a second set of tracks was made, mostly within the in-filled dinosaur tracks. It all hardened into rock which has now been exposed by erosion. The material which filled the dinosaur tracks was more resistant. This differential erosion explains the slightly raised dinosaur tracks. The platform also included 150 dinosaur tracks.

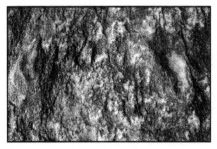

Track #4 in a series of 15 displays all five toes, instep, and heel, surrounded by dramatic "mud push-up" typical of real footprints, but not erosion. The depressed print extends into a slightly raised dinosaur track similar to the one just inches to the left. This sequence of tracks displays a right-left pattern and is consistent in length (about 10").

I have personally studied the Paluxy footprints at length since 1997. The sum total of the finds along the Paluxy reveals that man and dinosaurs did indeed live at the same time. The Paluxy footprints continue to be one of the major catalysts in the creation/evolution debate.

THE A. M. COFFEE TRACK

In 2006, a Permian age rock containing a human footprint eight and a half inches long and a child's print five inches long was donated to the Creation Evidence Museum. It is of Cambrian (pre-dinosaur) age which is approximately 290–245 million years ago. The track is thought to be one in a trail of nine other footprints found on a rock ledge outside Stinnett, Texas, in 1934, by Mr. A. M. Coffee.

Coffee worked loose one of the slabs of rocks displaying the footprint. It is not known if any photographs or maps of the trail were made when the track was *in–situ*. The Coffee print has created an instant controversy among archaeologists, geologists, and anthropologists because the sedimentary rock system of the entire area is geologically assigned to the Permian.

The track was donated to the Creation Evidence Museum and underwent spiral CT scan analysis. Compression areas were noted under the track and between the toes. The staff also observed three arches (medial, lateral, and metatarsal), and the overall distinctive shape of the human foot.

Dr. Baugh comments:

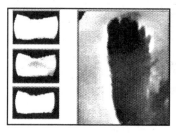

Attention was drawn to the depressions made by the dominant "great toe," the unique "second toe" that makes a slightly deeper depression, and the distinctive "ball" of the foot. When the analysis was complete the CT scan had recorded the compression around the complete footprint, clearly indicating that the print was not carved or fabricated. In CT scan X–rays the lighter areas are [denser], since the X–rays have more difficulty traveling through that medium.[172]

Dr. Baugh also emphasizes that the Coffee slab shows "a thin crustal layer of sediment formed over the bulk rock as both layers lithified. The crustal layer followed the contour of the contour of the depression. This thin layer is clearly seen, since a section of it peeled off as Mr. Coffee was removing the artifact. Any carving activity would have cut through the outer layer, clearly leaving its evidence of fabrication."

172. Baugh, Carl E, 2006, "What's New at CEM" article on Coffee Print at: http://www.creationevidence.org/cemframes.html.

The surface lamination exhibits this characteristic, which was deposited at the same time as the underlying rock.

THE DELK TRACK

Alvis Delk Print
in the Sir George Series

Photo: David Lines, Creation Evidence Museum

This spectacular fossil footprint was found in July of 2000 by amateur archaeologist Alvis Delk and is now on display at the Creation Evidence Museum in Glen Rose, Texas. Delk found the loose slab against the bank of the Paluxy River, about one mile north of Dinosaur Valley State Park. He flipped over the rock and saw an excellent dinosaur track, so he took it home where it sat in his living room for years, with hundreds of other fossils.

In early 2008, he decided to clean the track as it still had a layer of dried mud on it. What Delk thought was just a dinosaur track was indeed something more remarkable. After cleaning the rock, he discovered that the dinosaur track was actually stepping into a secondary track: a fossil human footprint! He brought it to the Creation Evidence Museum for further verification.

The track was scrutinized by a series of scientific tests to determine its authenticity, which included spiral CT scans. Spiral CT scans generate images of the inside of an object from a large series of two-dimensional X-ray images taken around a single axis of rotation. This technology provides an effective means of analyzing fossil footprints without physically destroying them. It allows us to see inside the rock, specifically, under the footprint.

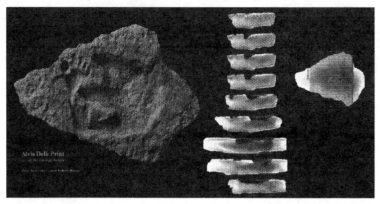

Over 800 X-ray images document density changes within the rock that correspond precisely with the fossil footprints. According to Ian Juby, president of CORE (Citizens for Origins Research and Education) in Ontario, Canada, these X-rays show distinct high-density areas in the rock immediately surrounding and underneath the tracks. Carving the tracks would have cut through the harder surface layer and would be visible in the X-rays. The other typical claim of skeptics is that forgers in the past used acid to etch the rock after carving a dinosaur track, to hide the tool marks in the rock. Acid etching would actually reduce the surface density of the rock and would be visible in the X-rays.[173]

Furthermore, Juby explains:

» the surface hardness is *absent* from many places in the rock
» the highest density rock is at the junction of the middle dinosaur toe and the human footprint, where both tracks would have compressed the matrix. It is up to four centimeters deep and wide at this point (see above). This makes complete sense if the tracks are both authentic—both footprints compressed that area of mud. This makes no sense when trying to explain it as artifacts like beam hardening, as this is the *only* place where such large-area,

173. http://ianjuby.org/delk/.

high–density is visible.

» there are portions of the tracks which do not have any surface hardening. Thus, it is clear that the higher density seen elsewhere is quite real. To claim that portions of the tracks show no higher density and thus must have been carved is a ludicrous argument: Did the carver only carve *portions* of the tracks? What about the portions that do show higher density and are therefore legit? No —the *variations in density* only add to the authenticity of the density readings.

Of course, carvings would show no corresponding structures beneath them. The existence of following contours beneath the fossil footprints dramatically demonstrates the authenticity of both tracks. The human footprint had been made first, and shortly thereafter (before the mud turned to stone), a dinosaur stepped in the mud with its middle toe stepping on top of the human track. You can actually see the displaced mud from the dinosaur's middle toe inside the human footprint.

According to evolutionary theory, dinosaur and humans are separated by millions of years. Of course, dinosaurs and humans cannot be stepping in each other's footprint if they are millions of years

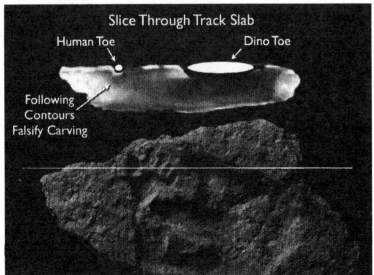

apart. These footprints provide profound evidence refuting the evolutionary myth.

Arizona

In the late 1960s, a private plane flown by Earl Cummings made an emergency landing on a dirt road along the Moenkopi Wash near the Little Colorado River of northern Arizona. While there, Cummings discovered some fossil tracks in sandstone which appeared to be that of a barefoot human child. Near it were some dinosaur tracks. Cummings recognized the strata as belonging to the Kayenta of the Glen Canyon Group, part of the Colorado Plateau which evolutionists date to about 200 to 175 million years before present. He wanted to return to the location, but never had the time or funds for an expedition. Years passed.

In 1984, Lorraine Austin found similar tracks not far from Cumming's site and told Paul Rosnau about them. That same year, Rosnau visited the area (later designated as *site–1*). There he located many human tracks, dinosaur tracks, and the handprint of a child that had slipped and put his hand down to catch himself.

Learning about Cumming's discovery, Rosnau received directions to his site, which turned out to be about 1.86 miles from site–1. In 1986 he searched for the Cummings site but was unable to locate the trackways, apparently because the dirt road had been widened and they had been eradicated. But about 100 yards west of the road, he found dozens of fossil human tracks. This location was named *site–2*.

The Arizona tracks are located in the Glen Canyon Group, which is part of late Triassic to early Jurassic strata and supposedly date to 200 to 175 million years ago. At least 300 tridactyl dinosaur tracks have been found there, a cloven–footed hoofprint of a mammal, bivalves (clams of the *Unlo complanatus*, a freshwater bivalve which still lives in American lakes), large amphibians, lungfish, and three ungulate–like tracks (domestic sheep or wild big horn sheep).

In the September 1989 issue of the *Creation Research Society Quarterly*, Rosnau, Auldaney, Howe, and Waisgerber published a 30–page article concerning the "quasi–human ichnofossils" found at an

Indian roadside stand near Tuba City, Arizona.[174] A number of photographs are included.

They did a second follow-up report in the December 1989 issue of some other tracks found nearby.[175] Here are some interesting comments by the authors:

"[Describing one of the tracks] The other was an almost perfect barefoot track, typical of tracks made in soft mud. It has a deep heel, an arch almost level with the surface, a deep ball, and toe angle" (*op. cit.*, part 2, p. 81).

"Similarly, a lone, indistinct, eroded dinosaur track would not be considered authentic, but in an area of distinct tracks it would be accepted as one of many genuine tracks. The trails of man-tracks we have located together with the details of the human foot—toes, ball of foot, arch, heel and taper of toes—rule out chance formations of nature in a great many of our discoveries"(*op. cit.*, p. 91).

"[Here are] two characteristics of authentic human footprints: (1) on hard surfaces they will assume an hourglass shape; (2) on wet surfaces the heel and ball of the foot will make prominent impressions while the arch will not be prominent. I submit that at site-2 at Tuba City there are tracks that meet both these qualifications" (*ibid.*).

"Among the impressions there are 30 that are better than the accepted human tracks displayed in the San Bernardino County Museum in Redlands, California" (*ibid*).

"There is a predominance of fossil bones and tracks of flesh-eating animals such as the phytosaurs, dinosaurs, Dilophosurus, and Coelophysis. In normal ecological systems, there are always more plant eaters. Does this indicate that these carnivorous animals had come down to the area to eat the dead killed in a cataclysm?" (*op. cit.*, p. 93).

A remarkable number of the tracks had sandals or something shoe-shaped on them.

---

174. Siegler, H. R., *Evolution or Degeneration: Which?* (1972), p. 83.
175. Leakey, Mary D., "Footprints in the Ashes of Time," *National Geographic,* April 1979, pp. 452–456.

"(1) There are trackways with repeated barefoot tracks while others have shoe prints which are always headed in the same direction and in reasonable stride with each other. (2) Some are almost identical, existing side by side with the right distance and angles to each other. (3) There are impressions with sharp, shoe–shaped outlines. (4) There is an unusually high percentage (22 percent) of foot and shoe–like impressions in groups. . . . (8) There are other print pairs with strikingly identical features, always near each other" (*op. cit.*, p. 92).

These tracks are about 100 feet away from a large set of dinosaur tracks. Over 60 human tracks were mapped and photographed. A number of the human tracks were in stride areas, some were standing still with left and right foot near each other, all the rest were walking and going somewhere.

New Mexico
White Sands

In 1931 near Alamogordo, New Mexico, Ellis Wright, a government trapper, discovered human footprints in the Tularosa Basin on the shore of old Lake Otero. The initial discovery was made in a small area on the west shore of Lake Otero. Since then, similar footprints have been found along a long stretch of the old shore. The footprints examined by scientists back in 1981 have almost eroded away.

The trail of 13 tracks stride across the muddy terrain measuring 22 inches long with a pace of four to five feet. Many dubbed the giant who made the footprints the "Tularosa Sasquatch." The now–dry lake existed at the end of the last ice age and covered hundreds of square miles of the Tularosa Basin. White Sands National Monument sits on the south end of the old lake and Northrup Strip, where the space shuttle landed in 1982, sits on the north end of the lakebed.

Dr. [Clifford] Burdick also tells about one of the unsolved mysteries of the Great White Sands National Monument near Alamogordo, New Mexico. Here is an area of about 175 acres consisting of alabaster, white as snow. It is believed that this gypsum was precipitated as arid winds dried up an inland sea. As this muddy sediment was beginning to harden, some prehistoric giant apparently walked across the drying lakebed, leaving a series of tracks made by sandaled feet. There are 13 human tracks, each track approximately 22 inches long and from 8 to 10 inches wide. The stride is from four to five feet."[176]

Later study of the footprints by state scientists revealed the footprints belonged to prehistoric camels and elephants (mammoths). They date from 8,000 to 13,000 years B.C.

What is unusual about these tracks is that they are in the form of pedestals about four to six inches tall. Scientists say the animals walked along the shore of the lake and made regular tracks in the mud. Because of their weight they compressed the mud under the track and made that material harder than the surrounding mud.

Now, as the shoreline erodes because of wind and rain, the surrounding material wears away faster than the footprints. This leaves the footprints standing several inches above the rest of the shore.

Pete Eidenbach with Human Systems Research, the missile range's archaeological contractor, says they have examined gullies along the shore and found subsurface footprints. In other words, the footprints were covered over with mud and silt and will probably come to the surface sometime in the future when the shoreline erodes more.

THE ZAPATA TRACK

In 1987, paleontologist Jerry MacDonald discovered a human fossil footprint in the Robledos Mountains of New Mexico. Among the discovery were a number of fossilized tracks from many different species of animals and birds evidently in Permian rock with an assigned evolutionary age of 248 to 290 million years ago. The footprint is called the "Zapata track" and is sharply out-

176. Siegler, H. R., *Evolution or Degeneration: Which?* (1972), p. 83.

lined in an hour-glass shape. The print shows some mud up-push. Joe Taylor briefly discusses the Zapata print in his book *Fossil Facts and Fantasies* (Taylor, 1999). He comments that it "appears to be a female, barefoot print." He states that it was found in 1929, and that "it is said that at that time, one half of a second track was visible at the edge of the ledge bearing both tracks. The edge of this ledge has since fallen off."

According to the evolutionary theory, the Permian was millions of years before animals, birds, and even dinosaurs existed and over 200 million years before the evolution of man occurred. The *Smithsonian Magazine* featured an article on the discovery in July 1992 (vol. 23, pg 70) titled "Petrified Footprints: A Puzzling Parade of Permian Beasts." The article acknowledged "what paleontologists like to call, problematica." It described what appeared to be large mammal and bird tracks that "evolved long after the Permian period, yet these tracks are clearly Permian."

The discovery of animal trackways in the Permian strata of New Mexico is documented at the Worldwide Museum of Natural History. No mention is made of the Zapata track or the conflict in dates between the existence of humans and animals in an ancient rock layer in which it is not supposed to exist.

FRANCE

Recent exploration of the Chauvet Cave near Vallon-Pont-d'Arc in southern France has yielded what scientist are claiming are the oldest footprints of Cro-Magnon man, and a cavern with a dozen new animal figures. The footprints appear to be those of an 8-year-old boy. They are assigned an evolutionary age between 20,000 and 30,000 years old, perhaps twice as old as those discovered previously at Aldene, Montespan, Niaux, Pech Merle, and other Upper Paleolithic sites.

The footprints were discovered by a team of 15 scientists who were studying the cave paintings. The markings, which measure 8.3 inches long, are thought to have been made by a boy eight to ten years old according to prehistorian Michel-Alain Garcia of the Center National de la Recherche Scientifique, Nanterre. Scientists estimate that the boy was about four and a half feet tall, his feet more than eight inches long, and three and a half inches wide.

First spotted in 1994 by Jean-Marie Chauvet, the cave's discoverer, the footsteps stretch perhaps 150 feet and at times cross those of bears and wolves. The steps lead to the so-called room of skulls, where a number of bear skulls have been found. In a few places there is evidence that the boy slipped on the soft clay floor, though Garcia says the prints show the boy was not running, but walking normally. The boy appears at one point to have stopped to clean his torch, charcoal from which has been dated to 26,000 years ago according to C14 dating. The prints from the Chauvet Cave, like nearly all footprints thus far discovered in Paleolithic caves, are from bare feet, which has led scholars to speculate that people of the time either left footwear at cave entrances or carried them.

Meanwhile, a team of 15 specialists, directed by French prehistorian Jean Clottes, recently investigated an uninventoried room originally discovered by Chauvet. There they found a dozen new paintings of mammoth, bison, and horses, among other animals. Clottes' team has so far documented 447 animals of 14 different species. By comparison, Niaux Cave in the French Pyrenees, cited by the French Paleolithic specialist Abbé Breuil as one of the half-dozen great caves containing prehistoric art, has 110 images images of six species.

TENNESSEE

JAGUAR CAVE

Jaguar Cave is a complex cave system in north central Tennessee. A total of 274 relatively complete footprints were found in the passage's moist surface when the passage was rediscovered approximately 30 years ago.

Most of the prints appear to have been made by bare, unshod feet. However, one of the prehistoric cavers may have been wearing some sort of footgear. The footprints are not continuous. These gaps in the footprint trail were caused by the prehistoric cavers walking on harder portions of the cave floor, where their feet left no impressions. Charcoal collected from a dry passage yielded dates of roughly 5,000 years ago, of the supposed Late Archaic period (Robbins, Wilson, & Watson, 1981).

The trails generally follow the most easily traveled route through an area called Aborigine Avenue. Footprints indicate that the cavers simply walked through the passage, occasionally deviating from the easiest route to inspect cave passage features. Some of these detours, such as the examination of pits in the floor of the passage, may indicate attempts to find alternate routes through the cave as well as additional passages.

For example, at least one prehistoric caver walked to the edge of a pit, apparently examined the drop–off, and, finding no alternative passage, continued along Aborigine Avenue. In addition to such exploratory searches, one person deviated from the main route to inspect a fallen flowstone column. Following the inspection, the prehistoric caver returned to the trail that the others were making to the end of the easily traveled portion of Aborigine Avenue.

Detailed analysis of the footprints identified micro–erosional differences among some of them, suggesting that there were at least two trips into Aborigine Avenue. Aborigine Avenue was rediscovered by modern cavers as a part of their explorations in 1976. These combined trips involved nine adult individuals of both genders, and possibly an adolescent (Robbins, *et al*, 1981). Data collection for each footprint included three measurements (foot length, heel width, and ball width), and orientation into or out of the passage. The prints were also mapped in relation to one another.

Archaeologists and volunteers altered some of the prints during their fieldwork. As an example of an accidental modification, there is a modern handprint made during the archaeological work by a student researcher who lost her balance and fell toward one of the footprint areas. Both while the archaeological documentation was going on (1976–1986), and after it was completed, modern cavers walked over some of the prints, altering and modifying them. Sometime between 1996 and 2002, a modern caver ignored the sign at the entrance of Aborigine Avenue and the surveying tape circling the prehistoric footprints and walked across them, altering at least five of the eleven prints near a pit edge. Today, nearly all of the prehistoric footprints display at least some modern damage. In addition to the human visitors, a dog, apparently accompanying a late 1970s caving party, entered Aborigine Avenue and its paw prints are now present among some of the prehistoric human footprints near the passage entrance.

Systematic photography offers a time–tested method for recording the footprints. Although selected prints and footprint areas were photographed during the original archaeological work, photographs of all prints in all areas are needed. This would provide a permanent record for each print, and of the prints' relations to each other and to cave features. For example, Charles Swedlund (1995, n.d.) used a photographic mosaic in Gothic Avenue, Mammoth Cave, Kentucky, to document 4,300 historic names on a long expanse of the ceiling. Using a series of overlapping images made by a camera on a track system, he captured the entire ceiling on one photographic mosaic.

A similar approach could be applied to ancient pathways on the floor of Jaguar Cave. Stereographic photogrammetry is similar in many ways to conventional photography. One of the advantages is that it documents images in three dimensions, producing fine–grained topographic maps. Depths and other three–dimensional details can be observed and measured from the topographic images. Photogrammetry has been successfully applied to the footprints at Laetoli, Tanzania.[177]

Automated laser scanning is an even more recently developed technique that also provides a permanent, high–resolution, three–dimensional record. Once at the site, it is quick, relatively inexpen-

---

177. Agnew N., & M. Demas, 1998, "Preserving the Laetoli footprints," *Scientific American,* v. 279, n. 3, p. 44–55.

sive, and avoids some of the problems associated with photography and photogrammetry. It is more precise than either and avoids problems with lighting and the time–consuming setup required by the other techniques. Resulting data can be manipulated electronically to permit accurate measurements, to show spatial relationships, and to produce three dimensional models. For example, an Upper Paleolithic carved horse on a rock shelter wall at Cap Blanc, France, was laser scanned to create a three–dimensional model.[178]

Ideally speaking, photographic, stereographic photogrammetric, and laser scanning approaches should all be applied to the Jaguar Cave footprints to preserve the maximum amount of information.

OTHER CAVES WITH FOOTPRINTS

The Jaguar Cave prehistoric footprints, extraordinary as they are, are not unique. Fossil footprints have been found in at least six other southeastern U.S. caves.

» Third Unnamed Cave, Tennessee
» Upper Crouchway, Unknown Cave, Kentucky
» Fisher Ridge Cave, Kentucky
» Sequoyah Caverns, Alabama
» Footprint Cave, Virginia
» Lon Odel Memorial Cave, Missouri

What sets Jaguar Cave apart from Unknown Cave and other southeastern footprint caves is that the foot impressions in Jaguar Cave are the greatest in number and the best documented (Robbins, *et al*, 1981). They have been systematically mapped, there are three radiocarbon dates associated with them, some of the impressions have been photographed, and all of the more complete prints have been measured. The Jaguar Cave footprints number more than those in all the other footprint caves in the southeastern U.S. combined.

178. Brown, K. A. R., A. Chalmers, T. Saigol, C. Green, & F. d'Errico, 2001, "An automated laser scan survey of the Upper Paleolithic rock shelter of Cap Blanc," *Journal of Archaeological Science,* v. 28, p. 283–289.

UTAH
THE MEISTER TRACK: ANTELOPE SPRINGS

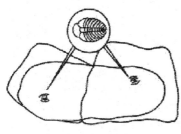

An unexpected sandal print

What may well be the oldest fossil footprint ever discovered was found in 1968 by William J. Meister, an amateur fossil collector. He was searching for trilobite fossils in the mountains of Utah. Breaking off a large, two-inch thick piece of rock, he hit it on its edge with a hammer, and it fell open in his hands. To his great astonishment he found inside a human footprint stepping on trilobites. The other half of the rock slab showed an almost perfect mold of a footprint and fossils. Amazingly, the human was wearing a sandal!

The footprint measured ten and a quarter inches long by three and a half inches wide at the sole and three inches wide at the heel. The heel print was indented in the rock about an eighth of an inch more than the sole. It was clearly the right foot, because the sandal was well-worn on the right side of the heel. Several easily visible trilobites were on the footprint. It had stepped on them, pressing them underfoot.

Thoroughly shaken, he took other men back who confirmed it and found still more, including some with sandals stepping on trilobites.

If the print is what it appears to be, the impression of a sandaled shoe crushing a trilobite, it would have had to have been made 300 to 600 million years ago, and would be sufficient to either overturn all conventionally accepted ideas of human and geological evolution or to prove that a shoe-wearing biped from another world had once visited this planet.

Trilobites are small marine creatures that flourished for over 320 million years before becoming extinct 280 million years ago. Evolutionists tell us that trilobites are one of the most ancient creatures which have ever lived on Planet Earth, and they existed millions of years before there were human beings.

SANDAL/SHOE PRINT FOUND IN CAMBRIAN STRATA, 43 MILES NORTWEST OF DELTA, UTAH, 1968. EMBEDDED IN THE TOE AND HEAL ARE TWO TRILOBITES. MANY PRINTS LIKE THIS HAVE BEEN FOUND AT THIS LOCATION, LESS THE EMBEDDED TRILOBITES

Humans are currently thought to have begun emerging between 1 and 2 million years ago and to have been wearing well shaped footwear for only the last several thousand. The sandal that seems to have crushed a living trilobite was ten and three–quarters inches long and three and a half inches wide; the heel is indented slightly more than the sole, as a human footprint would be. Meister took the rock to Melvin Cook, a professor of metallurgy at the University of Utah, who advised him to show the specimen to university geologists. When Meister was unable to find a geologist who was willing to look at the fossil, he went to the local newspaper, *The Desert News*. Before long, the find received national publicity. In a subsequent news conference James Marsden, the curator of the Museum of Earth Science at the University of Utah, said; "There were no men 600 million years ago. Neither were there monkeys or ground sloths to make pseudo human tracks. What man thing could have possibly been walking around on this planet before vertebrates even evolved?" Madsen then went on to say that the fossil must have been formed through natural processes, though what kind he was unable to suggest. Dr. Jesse Jennings, of the university's anthropology department, guessed (rather boldly, considering the absence of any supporting visual evidence) that the print might have been made by one large trilobite coming to rest on three smaller ones.

On July 20, 1968, the Antelope Spring site was examined by Dr. Clifford Burdick, a consulting geologist from Tucson, Arizona, who soon found the impression of a child's foot in a bed of shale. "The impression" he said "was about six inches long, with the toes spreading, as if the child had never yet worn shoes, which compress the toes. There does not appear to be much of an arch, and the big toe is not prominent." The print was shown to two geologists and one paleontologist. One of the geologists agreed that it appeared to be that of a human being, but the paleontologist said that no biological agent had been involved. Dr. Burdick stuck to his guns: "The rock chanced to fracture along the front of the toes before the fossil footprint was found. On cross section the fabric of the rock stands out in fine laminations, or bedding planes. Where the toes pressed into the soft material, the laminations were bowed downward from the horizontal, indicating a weight that had been pressed into the mud."

In August 1968 Mr. Dean Bitter, an educator in the Salt Lake City public school system, claimed to have found two more footprints in the Antelope Springs area. According to Dr. Cook, no trilobites were injured in these footfalls, but a small trilobite was found near the prints in the same rock, indicating that the small sea creature and the sandaled traveler might have been contemporaries (*Bible Science Newsletter*, August–September 1969; *Royal Research Society Quarterly*, December 1968; *CRSQ*, 1968, 5:3, p.97). The strata were primarily Cambrian, which is supposed to be the oldest on the planet. Leland Davis, a consulting geologist, analyzed the strata and the footprints discovered in it and found them to be "consisting almost entirely of Cambrian strata"!

The tracks do seem to represent a sandaled foot with a very distinguished heel imprint. If the prints are genuinely human, the theory of evolution is wrong and humans have either existed on the Earth for over 280 million years or the trilobites did not become extinct until the recent past. One other note is that the prints were found in a vertical position high on a steep angled wall, which means that if they are footprints, the area had been severely uplifted and tilted after they were formed.

HAWAII
KEONEHELELEI PRINTS

In 1857 Frederick S. Lyman, a 19–year–old tax assessor, was traveling around Hawaii Island estimating the age of individuals being taxed. Most Hawaiians did not know their date of birth nor their specific age but could associate their births with famous past events. So, as he carried out his assessment, Lyman recorded the information given to him by the natives. This list served as a means of consistently estimating the ages of individuals. In this list, five events were recorded to have occurred in the year 1790. Amongst these events is one buried within the list called Keonehelelei, "the falling sands."

In 1919, Ruy H. Finch, a geologist at the Hawaiian Volcano Observatory, discovered human footprints fossilized in the Ka'u desert ash. The discovery of the prints was purely accidental. In 1919 lava from Halemaumau drained out of the crater and erupted in an area of the Ka'u Desert. The eruption built a hill called Mauna Iki. Although the eruption area was only three miles from the then Hilo-Kona road, to get to Mauna Iki, Finch and his crew had to walk nearly twelve miles through the desert. A shorter route was available, but if the crew chose to access this route they had to walk over the very rough Keamoku'a'a flow. While walking through this shorter route, Finch discovered human footprints preserved in the hardened desert ash. Afterward, in 1938, this area of the desert became part of the Hawaii National Park. Several explosive eruptions of Kilauea have contributed to the Keanakakoi formation starting in about A.D. 1500. The latest major explosive eruption was probably in 1790.

Thus, the Keanakakoi ash is now thought as comprising of pyroclastic layers deposited between about 1500 and 1790 in recorded history. However, potassium–argon dating of the volcanic ash dates the pyroclastic layers 13–29 million years ago! The Keonehelelei footprints demonstrate conclusively that modern footprints are found in supposedly ancient rock.

AFRICA
THE LAETOLI TRACKS

 Human tracks from Laetoli in East Africa are described in the April 1979 issue of *National Geographic* and the February 9, 1980, issue of *Science News.* This significant archaeological find has created excitement and controversy about mankind's origins: excitement because of the archaeological find, and controversy about who made the tracks. Mary Leaky has suggested that these tracks were made by *Au. afarensis.*

Mary Leakey, the wife of the famous anthropologist Louis Leakey, found these fully human footprints in rock in 1974–1975 in Laetoli, Tanzania, which supposedly dates to 3.6 million years ago (Pliocene age) according to potassium–argon dating.[179]

"At a site called Laetoli in Kenya, 30 miles south of Olduvai Gorge, in 1976–1978, [Mary Leakey] made what she considers the most exciting discovery of her career: preserved footprints of three hominid

---

179. Wong, Kate, (August 01, 2005). "Flat feet and doubts about makers of the Laetoli tracks," *Scientific American.* Retrieved on 2007-04-20.

individuals who had left their tracks in soft volcanic ash more than 3 million years ago. It is a remarkable record of 'fossilized' behavior, establishing that very ancient man–like creatures walked exactly as we do" (Milner, 1990, p. 270).

"Mary Leakey has found at Laetoli in Africa, footprints which are considered to date from nearly 4 million years ago, and are identical with the footprints of modern humans except that they are some-what smaller.[180]

The discovery of the distinctly human footprints generated an outbreak of interest in scientists hoping to clear up the "posture de-bate." However, the prints look just like yours and mine. In fact, at least two individuals were present, walking along side each other. After almost five years of excavations Mary discovered three sets of well–fossilized footprint trails, preserved in the scorched Tanzanian ground, which she thought were made by two adults and one child.

How They Were Made

Sometime in the distant past a volcanic ash layer was deposited over the Laetoli region. The human inhabitants of the area walked across this thick, soft ash, leaving a trail of deep footprints as evidence of their occupation. The ash hardened, then filled with windblown sand. The intense heat of the African sun oven–baked the prints as if in a kiln and fossilized the impressions.

Evolutionists are astounded at the find, but cannot believe the evidence before them: that humans were alive when such ancient stratum was formed and saber–toothed tigers lived. On the same level with the footprints were prints of extinct creatures, such as the saber–toothed cat. Nevertheless, scientist still hold to the belief that Laetoli demonstrates incontrovertibly that 3.6 million years ago early humans were bipedal.

Conversely, a Royal Society paper by four scientists, including Dr Weijie Wang at Dundee University, said it appeared that Lucy and

---

180. Leakey, Mary O., "Footprints Frozen in Time," *National Geographic,* 155 (4): 446–457(1979).

other *australopithecines* walked like humans.[181] There are still some people who argue that, looking at the anatomy of the foot bones of *afarensis,* they were unlikely to have made the Laetoli footprints. And scientists still can't even agree on the posture of *Au. afarensis.* Evolutionists admit that they look exactly like human footprints, and say they are in 3.6 million year old rock, but refuse to accept them as made by humans, because to do so would destroy all their strata dating theories.

One desperate scientist rented a trained bear and had him dance around in wet mud in the hope the print would look like the human prints found in solid shale. His conclusion was that the Laetoli prints were identical to those of regular people.

They might, in fact, be identical to the footprints of a modern female in her teens. Moreover, Mary Leakey and Dr. Johanson have found teeth and jawbones which, except that they are again a little smaller, are virtually identical to modern humans. These remains, found at Laetoli and Hadar, date from about 3.75 million years ago. At Hadar, Johanson also found the bones of a hand "uncannily like our own" dated to about 3.5 million years ago.[182] "[In 1982, Richard Leakey] was also convinced from the famous foot prints at Laetoli that the genus *Homo* existed 3.75 million years B.C. (700,000 years before Lucy)."[183] Here are additional comments in the *National Geographic* article:

"They looked so human, so modern, to be found in tuffs so old," says footprint expert Dr. Louise Robbins of the University of North Carolina, Greensboro. "The best-preserved print shows the raised arch, rounded heel, pronounced ball, and forward-pointing big toe necessary for walking erect. Pressures exerted along the foot at-

---

181. "Robotics show Lucy walked upright," http://news.bbc.co.uk/go/pr/fr/-/1/hi/sci/tech/4697977.stm, Published: 2005/07/20.

182. Mehlert, A. W., "The *Australopithecines* and (Alleged) Early Man," *Creation Research Society Quarterly,* June 1980, p. 24.

183. Mehlert, A. W., News note, *Creation Research Society Quarterly,* December 1985, p. 145.

test to a striding gait. Scuff marks appear in the toe area, and a fossilized furrow seams the footprint. The footsteps come from the south, progress northward in a fairly straight line. The crispness of definition and sharp outlines convince me that they were left on a damp surface that retained the form of the foot."

The form of this foot was exactly the same as ours. On the same level with the footprints and close to them, trackers identified gazelles and other creatures almost indistinguishable from present–day inhabitants, but the saber–toothed cat and the clawed chalicothere, both now extinct, roamed with them. Dr. Louise Robbins of the University of North Carolina, Geensboro, an anthropologist who specializes in the analysis of footprints, visited Laetoli and concluded: "Weight bearing pressure patterns in the prints resemble human ones."[184]

Nevertheless, evolutionists remain adamant that *australopithecines* like Lucy walked upright! However, the skeletal anatomy of *australopithecine* fossils indicates a stooped gait similar to the "rolling" knuckle–walk of chimps. In March 2000, *Nature* published a report that the fossil "Lucy" (*Au. afarensis*) had the same wrist anatomy as "knuckle–walking" chimpanzees and gorillas.[185]

There is no evidence that these footprints belonged to an *Au. afarensis* like Lucy. The models however, continue to incorrectly align Lucy's big toe like that of a human foot. In fact, using multivariate analysis, the anatomist Dr. Charles Oxnard has shown that the big toe actually sticks out as in chimpanzees. This new data shows empirically that the *australopithecine* fossil foot bones of Lucy could not have possibly made the footprints at Laetoli.

---

184. Leakey, Mary D., "Footprints in the Ashes of Time," pp. 452–456.
185. "Did Lucy walk on her knuckles?", www.exn.ca, 22 March 2000;Walk Like an Ape," http://abcnews.go.com/sections/science/DailyNews/knucklewalk000322.html, 22 March 2000; "Early Man walked on all fours," www.telegraph.co.uk, 23 March 2000; based on Brian G. Richmond and David S. Strait, "Evidence that humans evolved from a knuckle–walking ancestor," *Nature* 404 (6776), 23 March 2000.

Unfortunately, the public is misled by inaccurately reconstructed models of Lucy displayed in museums and in literature. The feet and hands are often portrayed as remarkably human. Many evolutionists, however, admit to these errors, acknowledging that *australopithecine* hands and feet were "not at all like human hands and feet; but rather having long curved fingers and toes."[186]

Furthermore, anatomist Dr. Fred Spoor and his colleagues at University College, London, performed CT scans of *australopithecine* inner ear canals which reflect posture and balance capability and proved that they could not walk habitually upright.[187]

Once you eliminate the misleading evolutionary assumptions that provide the basis for radioisotope dating, there is absolutely no evidence that the Laetoli prints predate humans.

According to the *Journal of Human Evolution* (2007), "Several researchers have estimated kinematic parameters of early hominin gait by comparing the Laetoli stride lengths with those of modern humans. . . . The majority of these stride–length analyses concluded that the Laetoli hominins must have used a gait similar to that of modern humans, since their stride lengths fit modern human models."

However, according to Johnson, the writer of the book named *Lucy*, these footprints should have been left by *Au. afarensis*. Do you wonder why? Because otherwise it would be a catastrophe for the evolutionists to accept that modern man lived in such an early date. Author and researcher Michael Cremo states in his abstract, *Forbidden Archeology of the Paleolithic* (1999):

> Leakey herself (1979:453) said the prints were exactly like anatomically modern human footprints, a judgment shared by other physical anthropologists (Tuttle 1981:91, 1987:517).

186. Menton, Dr. David, "'Ape–woman' statue misleads public: anatomy professor," *Creation* 19(1):52, Dec. 1996–Feb. 1997.
187. Spoor, F., B. Wood, and F. Zonneveld, "Implications of early hominid morphology for evolution of human bipedal locomotion," *Nature* 369(6482):645–648, 1994.

Tim White said, "Make no mistake about it. They are like modern human footprints" (Johanson and Edey, 1981:250). Attempts to account for the humanlike nature of the prints have varied. Some have suggested that late Pliocene hominids such as *Australopithecus afarensis* could have made the prints. But such proposals are not supported by skeletal evidence in the form of a complete *Australopithecus* foot. White and Suwa (1987) attempted to put together such a foot (using bones from three different hominids of different genera), but such an exercise was, of course, quite speculative.

In 1995, Clarke and Tobias reported the discovery of a partial *Australopithecus* foot from Sterkfontein (Bower 1995), and in 1998 announced the discovery of a fairly complete *australopithecine* skeleton, to which the foot bones had originally belonged. The four foot bones reported in 1995 made up a left instep. The big toe was long and divergent, like that of a chimpanzee, with features indicating it was capable of grasping. Like White and Suwa, Tobias and Clarke used bones from East African hominids to reconstruct a complete foot, which Tobias said matched the Laetoli prints (Bower 1995). Physical anthropologist Michael Day at the British Museum asserted that the Sterkfontein foot could not have made the Laetoli footprints and questioned the accuracy of a reconstruction that made use of bones of hominids from different parts of Africa (Bower 1995).

In January 1999, at the World Archaeological Congress in Cape Town, South Africa, Clarke attempted to justify how the chimpanzee–like Sterkfontein foot could have made the humanlike Laetoli prints. He explained that chimpanzees sometimes walk with their normally divergent big toes pressed inward so as to align with the other toes. These other toes, although longer than human toes, would have been curled under. But it is highly unlikely that the three individuals who made the trails of prints at Laetoli would have all been walking like that.

A similar proposal had earlier been made by Stern and Susman (1983). But others (Tuttle *1985:132*, White and Suwa 1987:495*)* pointed out that the prints showed no knuckle marks, and that surely, in the case of so many prints representing three individuals, some of the prints would have shown the extended toes. Clarke also pointed to a recent study by Deloison (1997) who claimed, in opposition to almost all previous reports, that the Laetoli prints displayed distinctly primate (chimpanzoid) features. Others (Tuttle, *et al,* 1998) answered, demonstrating that Deloison's observations were "false interpretations based on artifactual taphonomic features, reliance on a partial sample of the . . . first generation casts of the Laetoli prints, and her not accounting for the orientation of the prints on the trackway."

So it would appear reasonable to propose that anatomically modern humans made the Laetoli prints in the late Pliocene. This proposal becomes even more reasonable when we consider the other discoveries of evidence for anatomically modern humans in the Pliocene. Fairly complete anatomically modern human skeletons were discovered in Middle Pliocene clays at Castenedolo by the geologist Ragazzoni (1880), who testified that the overlying layers were undisturbed. European archeologists later rejected the discoveries on theoretical grounds.

For example, Macalister (1921:183) said, "There must be something wrong somewhere." Considering the anatomically modern character of the skeletons, he proposed (1921:184), "Now, if they really belonged to the stratum in which they were found, this would imply an extraordinarily long standstill for evolution. It is much more likely that there is something amiss with the observations."

It is very clear that these footprints belonged to actual human beings. These were human footprints, because apes do not have a heel bone. Paleoanthropologist Timothy White who worked with Mary Leakey again remarked: ". . . The external morphology is the same. There is a well–shaped modern heel with a strong arch and a good ball of the foot in front of it. The big toe is straight in line. It doesn't stick out to the side like an ape toe, or like the big toe in so many drawings you see of *Australopithecus* in books."[188]

---

188. Johanson and Edey 1981:250

	hominid 1	hominid 2
length of footprint	21.5 cm	18.5 cm
width of footprint	10 cm	8.8 cm
length of pace	47.2 cm	28.7 cm
reconstructed body–size	1.34–1.56 m	1.15–1.34 m

After examining the footprints, Louis Robins from North California University made the following comments: "The arch is raised—the smaller individual had a higher arch than I do—and the big toe is large and aligned with the second toe . . . the toes grip the ground like human toes. You do not see this in other animal forms."[189]

Russell Tuttle, who also examined the footprints, wrote: "A small barefoot *H. sapiens* could have made them. . . . In all discernible morphological features, the feet of the individuals that made the trails are indistinguishable from those of modern humans.[190]

These original measurements were made from a certified hard cast of the Laetoli footprint by Michael Reddick. After X–Y–Z dimensional measurements were run, the data was computer–generated to reveal a calibrated reproduction of the print. This reproduction of the footprint displayed features which are exclusively seen in the *H. sapien* footprint. These features are:

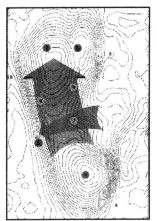

» calcaneus (heel)
» transverse arch
» lateral side of the longitudinal arch
» medial side of the longitudinal arch
» base of the fifth metatarsal
» first phalange (great toe)
» phalanges trench (digits 2–5), and
» areas of weight distribution

189. *Science News,* Vol 115, 1979, pp. 196–197
190. Anderson, Ian, *New Scientist,* Vol 98, 1983, p. 373

ARCH EXPRESSION IN THE LAETOLI FOOTPRINT

These areas of weight distribution correspond specifically and exclusively to mankind. They include: (1) the calcaneus heel section as the first area of impression in man's forward locomotion; (2) the lateral flange area along the outside of the foot toward the small toe, the second area of transfer impression in man's forward locomotion; and (3) the ball–great toe section along the inside of the foot, the third area of transfer impression in man's forward locomotion. These areas of weight distribution indicate that the individual making the footprints was not hominid, but true *H. sapien*. The implication of this research is that fully developed man was present in ancient times.

This situation put the Laetoli footprints at the center of discussions for years. Evolutionist paleoanthropologists desperately tried to come up with an explanation, as it was hard for them to accept the fact that a modern man had been walking on the Earth 3.6 million years ago. During the 1990s, the following explanation started to take shape. The evolutionists decided that these footprints must have been left by an *Australopithecus*, because according to their theory, it was impossible for a *Homo* species to have existed 3.6 million years ago. However, Russell H. Tuttle wrote the following in an article in 1990: "In sum, the 3.5 million–year–old footprint traits at Laetoli site G resemble those of habitually unshod modern humans. None of their features suggest that the Laetoli hominids were less capable bipeds than we are. If the G footprints were not known to be so old, we would readily conclude that they were made by a member of our genus *Homo*. . . . In any case, we should shelve the loose assumption that the Laetoli footprints were made by Lucy's kind, *Australopithecus afarensis*" (Tuttle, 1990, p. 61–64).

It was impossible for these supposed 3.6 million–year–old footprints to be Lucy's. There is no relation between the 3.6 million–year–old footprints and Lucy. The only reason why the footprints were thought to have been left by members of *Australopithecus* was the 3.6 million–year–old volcanic layer in which the footprints were found. The prints were ascribed to *Australopithecus* purely on the assumption that humans could not have lived so long ago! But because Lucy had curved hands and feet, and used its front feet while walking, Lucy could not have left these prints.

These interpretations of the Laetoli footprints demonstrate one important fact. Evolutionists support their theory not based on scientific findings, but in spite of them. Here we have a theory that is blindly defended no matter what. The footprints were certainly made by modern people like us. Examinations of the morphological form of the footprints show time and again that they are accepted as the prints of a modern human. These footprints consist of as many as 70 individual footprints in two parallel lines about 30 meters long. Impartial examinations on the footprints reveal their real owners. Plainly, they are human prints.

SOUTH AFRICA
THE LANGEBAAN LAGOON FOOTPRINTS

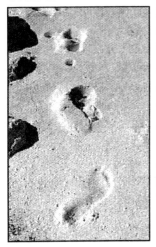

In the early autumn of 1995 in the West Coast National Park just north of Cape Town, a chance discovery was made of a sequence of human footprints, discovered by field geologist Dave Roberts on the shore of Langebaan Lagoon, in hardened sand dune deposits.[191]

There were two complete footsteps and the remnants of a third, eroded since they were exposed a few years before. They formed a right–left–right track descending diagonally down the dune face toward the lagoon, which was near when the prints were made. The stride length of 0.51 meters and the length of the feet themselves 0.22 meters (size 5 by today's standards) suggests that the person was a small female, probably about 1.6 meters tall. The feet had well-developed arches, and the

---

191. Gore, R., 1997. "The dawn of humans. Tracking the first of our kind." *National Geographic* 192 (3): 92–99.

big toe was the longest of the toes—all features of modern humans. The long axis of the right and left complete prints forms large angles to the direction of motion. This was caused by the waddling gait that the person had adopted to negotiate a sloping and unstable sandy dune. The steepness of the slope was reduced by walking diagonally rather than directly down the dune. Prominent ridges of sand, superbly preserved, had been squeezed up on the down–slope side of each print, formed at the instant of weight transfer during the stride.

According to scientists, the Langebaan Lagoon footprints are considered the oldest prints reliably ascribed to fully modern humans. The date is not a problem because there are no contradictions with the date and human evolution. These tracks do indeed display all the qualities of human footprints just as you would see on a sand beach today. Nevertheless, if scientists would have obtained a different date that skewed off the chart either way, it would throw the evidence into contradiction with the geologic time scale. The tracks would then have to be reclassified or the dates would be simply discarded all together.

The standard interpretation suggests that the prints date to the last interglacial period, which lasted supposedly from about 135–115,000 years ago. An initial luminescence date of 85,000 years ago seemed too young to some. Subsequently, Lee Berger, an anthropologist at Wits, became involved in the project and obtained further funding from *National Geographic.* Scientists were able to date the entire Cenozoic sequence at the site. The date was reassigned an age of 117,000 years.[192]

This age is highly significant because this date redefines the site to a critical period in human evolution when anatomically modern man was emerging from archaic types. According to the "out of Africa" theory of modern human origins, anatomically modern man evolved in Africa, subsequently dispersing to Eurasia and displacing the more primitive inhabitants, such as the Neanderthals, in the

---

192. Roberts, D., & L. R. Berger, 1997. "Last Interglacial (c. 117 Kr) human footprints from South Africa." *South African Journal of Science* 93(8): 349–350.

process. As a result, this leads people to believe the footprint-maker may have been ancestral to modern human populations. This of course, is false.

BRITISH COLUMBIA

Hidden in the laminated silts of the Severn Estuary foreshore at Goldcliff are 8,000–year–old (Mesolithic) human footprints. Goldcliff is a community parish to the southeast of the city of Newport in South Wales. Specialist Rachel Scales has been excavating the silts to uncover the fleeting snapshots of past human activity.

There are a large number of human footprint-tracks. They represent a range of individuals, from children as young as three years old to teenagers and adults. Several trails have been recorded, including one that revealed footprints of four children walking toward Goldcliff Island. A 5'6" man with size 11 feet walked along the Severn Estuary at 2.6 miles per hour carrying a heavy load on his right shoulder. Archaeologists deduced all this from a series of footprints cemented in the hard clay of the Severn Estuary. The footprint-covered sediments are layered in bands and, using a combination of sediment and pollen analysis, John Allen (from the University of Reading) and Petra Dark have demonstrated that each band represents one year, with a layer of coarse material in winter and a layer of fine material in summer. Some of the human footprints were clearly made in fine summer sediments.

USKMOUTH (NEWPORT)

Uskmouth is effectively in the west of the village of Nash. It is at Uskmouth that the River Usk meets the Severn Estuary. Following storms in the autumn of 1986, a track of human footprints was discovered

Photo by Mike Hally

eroding out of the clays in the intertidal zone in front of Uskmouth Power Station. The footprints were found to contain peat deposits which were carbon dated (C14) to a guesstimated date of 4200 B.C. According to evolutionary interpretation, this makes them the oldest known human footprints in Britain.

Scientific study has revealed that the man who left these prints had a shoe size equivalent to size 8.5. He stood about 1.70m tall (5.5 feet) and the way his big toe splays outwards indicates that he was accustomed to walking without shoes. The footprints have been preserved because very soon after he took his walk a period of hot, dry weather baked the mud on which he trod. This mud was then gradually covered over by a layer of peat which preserved them.

FORMBY POINT

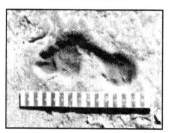

Coastal erosion has revealed the fossil footprints of humans (adult and child), animals (cattle, red deer, roe deer, unshod horse, dog, wild boar, sheep/goat), and wading birds preserved in the supposed late–Holocene silt exposures at Formby Point, Sefton Coast, Northwest England.

C14 and optically stimulated luminescence dating dates the prints in the late–Mesolithic to mid–Neolithic. However, a higher, dune–edge peat stratum contains the imprints of Iron Age domestic oxen.

Since 1989, an archive of over 3,000 photographs and other data relating to the paleoenvironment of Formby Point has been established. Of the 184 human footprint trails recorded to date, calculations would suggest a mean adult male height of 1.66m and a mean adult female height of 1.45m.

Gait analyses would seem to indicate the women and children were mainly occupied in gathering food (shrimp or other seafood, for example). Male footprints are sometimes directly associated with red and roe deer tracks. Evidence of an increased stride over the norm would suggest hunting activity.

ITALY

In 2003, scientists from the University of Padua identified three bipedal trackways descending a mountainous slope. Locals have known about the tracks for many years and have named it the "Devil's Trails." The tracks are nearly 1,000 feet up the side of Roccamonfino, a dormant volcano about 35 miles from Naples.

The 56 footprints are well preserved in the volcanic ash. The tracks are about eight inches long and less than four inches wide, showing deeply indented heel marks with indications of hand imprints out to the side, apparently to maintain their balance. One of the trails displays an amazing zigzag pattern, apparently attempting to negotiate the 80–degree slope without falling. Another shows the imprint of a long, deep gouge where the person was sliding down the steep slope for more than two feet. All three trails head the same direction—away from the crater.

The rock is composed of part sedimentary and part volcanic rock, known as a pyroclastic lava flow, which supposedly dates around 325,000 years ago. According to this date, scientists credit the find as being the oldest human footprints in the world. You may be asking yourself, "I thought the Laetoli Africa tracks were about 3.6 million? So why are these tracks classified as the oldest?"

Again, their reasoning is inferred by the dates they get from the rock. The problem is that these tracks are fully human in shape and appearance, but if you abide by the evolutionary dating system and family tree, you cannot have *H. sapiens* running around 325,000 years ago. Therefore, *H. sapiens* could not have possibly been around to make them.

Some are claiming that modern man did not emerge into the annals of history until approximately 200,000 years ago from the African continent. Therefore, they attribute the track makers to *H.*

heidelbergensis, a forerunner of Neanderthals, as the culprit (also known as the Stone Age Paleolithic archaic *H. sapiens*). But according to Professor Clive Gamble, director of the Center for Palaeolithic Archaeology at Southampton University in the UK, this "is interesting because the bone evidence of *heidelbergensis* is of a big, strapping lad 1.8 metres tall and weighing 100 kg."[193]

Scientists are only willing to conclude that the tracks belong to genus *Homo*. Dr. Paolo Mietto of Italy's University of Padua, the leader of the scientific group that analyzed the tracks, makes this statement: "[The Italian footprints] are the oldest footprints to be found of the genus *Homo*; not as old as those found in Tanzania—but the genus *Homo*. The footprints in question have one unique aspect: the ones found up to now have been on flat ground and this is on a slope."[194]

According to the footprint lengths, the estimated height of the individuals is less than five feet tall. However, scientists do not consider that these may be young, human adults. Their theory will not allow for this reasoning. They use the long dating ages and the small stature of the individual as evidence to declare these are hominid footprints. Nonetheless, the evidence of the footprints show these are fully human in form—nothing more and nothing less. Others say *H. erectus* made them, while still others say that these might represent a whole new classification. As a result, this presents a dilemma for the evolutionist. Scientists continue to squabble over what and who made the tracks.

Nicaragua
The footprints of Acahualinca

The footprints of Acahualinca were found close to Lake Managua near Managua, Nicaragua. They were located 16 to 24 feet below the surface, beneath eleven strata of solid rock. Construction workers discovered the footprints accidentally in 1874. Earl Flint, an Ameri-

---

193. Whitehouse, Dr. David, "Oldest human footprints found," http://news. bbc.co.uk/go/pr/fr/-/1/hi/sci/tech/2844287.stm.
194. Ibid.

can medical doctor and archaeological collector, brought the footprints to the attention of the international science community and media in 1884.[195]

Flint described the tracks in these words, written in 1884:

The footprints are from one–half to three inches in depth and none exceeded 18 inches. Some of the impressions are nearly closed, the soft surface falling back into the impression, and a crevice about two inches in width is all one sees, and my first glance at some parallel to one less deep, gave me an idea that the owner of the latter was using a stave to assist him in walking. In some the substance flowed outward, leaving a ridge around it—seen in one secured for the museum; the stride is variable, owing to the size of the person, and the changing nature of the surface passed over. The longest one uncovered was 17 inches, length of foot 10 inches, and width 4 inches, feet arched, steps in a right line, measured from center of heel to center of great toe over three steps. The people making them were going both ways in a direction consonant to that of the present lake shore east and west, more or less.[196]

The footprints are classified according to evolutionary time scale as Paleo–Indian of the Upper Paleolithic in the Pleistocene epoch. Remember, by classifying it this way, they would have you believe these footprints were made by archaic *H. sapiens* who were part of the Clovis culture—not modern humans.

---

195. Flint, Earl, (1884) "Human footprints in Nicaragua," *American Antiquarian* 6: 112–114; (1885) "Human footprints in Nicaragua," *American Antiquarian* 7: 156–158.

196. Flint, Earl, (1889) "Nicaragua Footprints" *American Antiquarian*, vol. 11, 306–311.

 Nevertheless, these are some of the best examples of fossilized human footprints, left behind by 15 people walking in volcanic ash and mud that solidified some 6,000 years ago. Initially, the prints were dated at 200,000 years. However, since the feet were perfectly modern, the age was reduced to about 50,000 years. Work was continued by Joaquín Matilló, Allan L. Bryan, and Jorge Espinoza in the 1960s and '70s. Allan L. Bryan, from the University of Alberta, dated the sand directly under the footprints by radiocarbon dating to 5,945±145 years.[197] This yielded a date approximately to 3000 B.C.

This means that in very recent times a catastrophic flood caused those thick layers of eleven rock strata to form above the prints. To make matters worse, fossils and mastodon bones have been found in the strata above the human prints. This indicates a global flood. In addition, fossilized footprints of several animals are also present, including dogs and horses, intersecting the human footprints. The Carnegie Institute of Washington began the first scientific analysis and excavations in 1941, and in 1942 they constructed a museum and a building to protect the footprints.[198]

In 1978, a Nicaraguan researcher, Jorge Espinoza, continued the excavation near the termination of the original excavation and uncovered more footprints at a depth of 13 feet. The tracks may continue further. Specimens of these footprints can be seen at both the Peabody Museum of Archaeology at Harvard University and the United States National Museum.[199] Incidentally, Harvard University

197. Bryan, Alan L., (1973) "New light on ancient Nicaraguan footprints," *Archaeology* 26 (2): 146–147.

198. Carnegie Institution of Washington. "Geologic observations on the ancient human footprints near Managua, Nicaragua." Contributions to *American Anthropology and History* 11 (52).

199. Brown, Roland W., US Geological Survey, Washington, D.C. (1947). "Fossil plants and human footprints in Nicaragua," *Journal of Paleon-*

has a sandal print that was found next to human and animal tracks, near the city of San Raphael.

AUSTRALIA

In 2003, an aboriginal woman of the Mutthi Mutthi tribe accidentally discovered dozens of timeless footprints along the borders of the Willandra Lakes system, a series of shallow, dry lakebeds in southeastern Australia. She was assisting Steve Webb, a biological archaeologist with Bond University in Queensland, in an archaeological survey of the area. The team found a clay area up in the dunes near one of the lakes, and found the first of what's turned out to be about 450 footprints over 700 square meters in Mungo National Park (about 195 miles from Broken Hill). The discovery is said to represent the largest collection of supposed Pleistocene human footprints in the world (Webb, Cupper, & Robins, 2006).

Webb determined that erosion had exposed 89 of the footprints. They excavated through soil to expose another 35 footprints. The tracks were made in silty clay containing calcium carbonate that hardened like concrete as it dried out. The tracks dried and were covered over by a further layer of clay and finally by meters of sand from shifting dunes.

The tracks, which are guestimated at 20,000 years, show people running, trotting, and walking on soft, wet ground. To estimate the age of the sediment, the team used a laser light on sand grains from just above and below the footprint soil layer. Light emissions then provide a measure of accumulated radioactivity, from which calculations are made. Again, these dating methods are not dependable and produce erroneous ages. In order to date artifacts or footprints in this case, scientists attempt to date the rock in which it is found by using false assumptions based on the geologic time table. So, in

tology 21 (1): 38–40. Retrieved on 2007-01-19.

order to date a fossil, one has to know the age of the rock. Therefore the reverse must be true. To date a rock or rock layer, one must identify what fossil or creature lived in that geologic time. This is called circular reasoning. Consequently, the end justifies the means.

There are presently estimated to be some 700 fossil footprints dispersed among the sand dunes of the now dry lake area; 400 of them clustered in a set of 23 tracks. The team has found 22 track ways, some up to 20 meters long, from where single people had walked in a line. The fact that people were walking in a single file shows high intelligence and reasoning.

Photo: Don Hitchcock

Most of the footprints were quite deeply impressed into the hardpan sediments, recording detailed features of foot morphology. Many have separate toe prints, and some preserve impressions of interphalangeal joint, heel and ball, and medial arch structures. Seventy-six of the footprints are contained within 8 trackways, with the remaining 48 prints seemingly randomly distributed. Footprint orientation indicates that people were moving in all directions across the site, although 65 percent of the prints are heading toward the northeast quadrant, with over three-quarters of prints pointing east.

—Webb, *et al*, 2006

The preservation of the tracks is quite remarkable. They reveal a very active group of people doing different things. There were trails of a group of six adults who ran in the same direction, another two people, a teenager and a child walking in the same general direction, and a one-legged man who left a trail of his right footprint only. There was no evidence of any crutch or support used by what would have normally been the left-sided footprint. Also, the prints of two kangaroos and a baby emu are in the immediate area. Other details included a set of small, round holes where a man stood with a spear, and squiggle lines in the mud, perhaps drawn by a child. The tracks are between 13cm and 30cm (size 11) in length. (Height= foot length X 6.585 plus or minus 0.495).[200]

"The relationship between foot length and height are not known for late Pleistocene peoples, but foot to stature correlations have been found to be almost universal among modern humans" (Webb, *et al*, 2006). In other words, this correlates with the modern anatomy of the human foot.

Katharine Hibbert writes in her article "A Step Back in Time," "The footprints vary in length from 6in to nearly 1ft; the smallest feet probably belonged to a child standing 3ft 5in high. The largest two group members, with feet of UK size 12 and 10, were about 6ft 6in and 6ft 4in tall, their impressive height corroborated by skeleton remains from a similar period, also discovered near the lakes."[201]

Steve Webb, a professor of Australian studies at Bond University who led the scientific team examining the footprints, said the use of ground penetrating radar had shown six different clay surfaces beneath the dune which might contain up to 2,500 footprints. Yet, more astonishing is that there could be as many as 5,000 more footprints underneath an adjacent sand dune.

Although scientists date the tracks at 20,000 years old, the Pleistocene epoch, keep in mind that this epoch is said to have been between 2 million to 12,000 years ago; the supposed rise of modern humans. By stating these tracks are Pleistocene, they would have you believe that these tracks belong to archaic *H. sapiens.* According to evolutionary interpretation, the earliest human settlers in Australia are believed to have arrived by sea from Indonesia about 50,000 years ago. Shouldn't sailing represent intellect, and thus high intelligence? Today, we have books that teach modern humans how to sail, for example *Sailing for Dummies.* Perhaps this shows evidence of devolution instead.

---

200. An anthropological rule of thumb holds that the length of the foot represents about 15 percent of an individual's height. Mary D. Leakey, "Footprints in the Ashes of Time," *National Geographic,* April 1979, p. 453.

201. www.smh.com.au, "A step back in time," December 23, 2005.

MEXICO

In the desolate and desert environment of Puebla, Mexico, lies a section of volcanic rock near the volcano Popocatépetl, which can be seen in the distance. Popocatépetl comes from the Nahuatl words *popōca*, "it smokes," and *tepētl*, "mountain," meaning "smoking mountain." This is the second highest peak in Mexico. In the summer of 2003, in an abandoned quarry in Mexico, 269 human footprints were found preserved in volcanic ash in the Valsequillo region of central Mexico.[202]

The archaeological find by Silvia Gonzalez, a geoarchaeologist at Liverpool John Moores University, has created its own volcano of controversy amongst scientists. Dr. Gonzalez found fossilized footprints near the city of Puebla while the team was working on dating and mapping the geology of the Valsequillo Basin.

The tracks are indisputably human, displaying arches, toe shapes, and sizes correctly for people four to six feet tall. It is estimated that more than a third of the prints were made by children. The remaining prints included various animals such as dogs, cats, possibly deer, camels, and cattle.[203]

The footprint site has created a new battle over history, from the first Americans in the Late Pleistocene/ Early Holocene epochs, to the last continent to be occupied by humans. Until recently most archaeologists believed the first arrivals were hunters and gathers from Asia who crossed some 11,000–13,500 years ago, when the Bering land bridge became available between Siberia and Alaska. However, Oxford University dated the sand grains embedded into the volcanic ash with a technique called the *optically stimulated luminescence* (OSL) method that records the last time the rock was exposed to heat or sunlight. The team also used rapid prototyping equipment and laser scans to create extremely accurate three–dimensional copies accurate to a fraction of a millimeter.

---

202. McAloon, C., "Footprints in Mexico create scientific stir," Associated Press, *Live Science*, www.livescience.com, 5 July, 2005.
203. Classifying the footprints, www.mexicanfootprints.co.uk/research/classifying.htm, 26 September, 2007.

The OSL method resulted in a date of about 40,000 years (Gonzalez, Huddart, Bennett, and Gonzalez–Huesca, 2006). This sent shockwaves throughout academic circles. This date challenges the evolutionary concept that the arrival of the first humans was in the Americas. This theory is based on the Clovis technology that is based on stone tools that were found in Clovis, New Mexico. The striking fluted spearpoints made by the Clovis people supposedly date back 11,500 years or so. They are believed to have been left by people who crossed a land bridge that once existed between Siberia and Alaska. David Huddart, co–investigator of Liverpool's John Moores, stated, "The existence of 40,000-year-old human footprints in Mexico means the 'Clovis First' model of human occupation can no longer be accepted as the first evidence of human presence in the Americas."[204] Now they have a problem with the date.

But it gets even better. Paul Renne, director of the Berkeley Geochronology Center and an adjunct professor of Earth and planetary science at UC Berkeley, and his colleagues report the argon technique gave an age of 1.3 million years (Renne, Feinberg and Waters; *et al*, 2005). "You're really left with two possibilities. One is that they are really old hominids—shockingly old—or they're not footprints."[205]

For the evolutionary mindset, this implies that humans were populating Central America 1.3 million years ago. Now, they are really in a dilemma. So here are the possibilities: (1) they are 1.3 million years old and are tracks of humans; (2) they are 41,500 years old and are human; and (3) they are not real tracks.

The sediment in question, called Xalnene ash by Gonzalez, *et al*, is a tough, somewhat sandy material used as building material today. It is described in Renne and Feinberg's article as tephra, moderately indurated olivine basalt lapilli tuff. This layer was dated by the 40Ar/39Ar dating method to around 1.3 million years.

Yet according to evolutionary theory, this date is far too old to be

204. Rincon, Paul, "Footprints of first Americans," http://news.bbc.co.uk/go/pr/fr/-/1/hi/sci/tech/4650307.stm.
205. Sanders, R., "Alleged 40,000-year-old human footprints in Mexico much, much older than thought," University of California, Berkley, www.eurekalert.org, 30 November 2007.

compatible with human footprints. Therefore, the footprints predate the first known appearance of the hypothetical *H. sapiens* in Africa by more than a million years!

Dr. Gonzalez, the discoverer of the prints, has studied the fossil human tracks in Lancashire and recognized that she could see similar characteristics in the volcanic ash. "Suddenly, I began to see some marks on the top surface of the ash ... and I recognized them as human footprints," she told the BBC's "Unearthing Mysteries" program. "I felt quite shocked, because I knew already that this ash was very old."

Dr. Gonzalez said that the "footprints were preserved as trace fossils in volcanic ash along what was the shoreline of an ancient volcanic lake. Climate variations and the eruption of the Cerro Toluquilla volcano caused the lake levels to rise and fall, exposing the Xalnene volcanic ash layer." She went on to say that the early Americans walked across this shoreline, leaving behind footprints that soon became covered in more ash and lake sediments. Then the trails became submerged when the water levels rose again and thus preserved the footprints.

Professor Dave Huddart at JMU compared the likeness to his own feet: "If I put my foot beside it, size 8½, it looks a typical size; it's got the characteristic figure–of–eight shape and the big toe is there, so it's a left foot."[206] Matthew Bennett at Bournemouth University in the UK clarifies, "They are unmistakably human footprints. They meet all the criteria that were set up after the Laetoli prints were found [in Tanzania in 1976]."[207]

Professor Renne also looked at the magnetization of the rocks to see if they might have been mixed up and redeposited from an earlier material. His conclusion: they were not. But he did find that the magnetic polarity was the opposite of the Earth's present magnetic field. Occasionally the Earth's magnetic poles do flip. "The last time

---

206. Redfern, Martin, "'Footprints' debate to run and run," http://news.bbc. co.uk/go/pr/fr/-/2/hi/science/nature/4617466.stm.
207. Adler, Robert, "Footprints rewrite history of first Americans," July 5 2005, www.newscientist.com/article.ns?id=dn7627.

the Earth's magnetic field had consistently reversed polarity was about 790,000 years ago, so the fact that we found reversed polarity magnetization in this rock tells us that it's older than 790,000 years," he said.[208]

On the other hand, there are those who dispute the findings. Those who disagree argue the current dating techniques are indeed problematic. In an analysis done by P. R. Renne and J. M. Feinberg (2005) they state, "We conclude that the identification of any of these features as syndepositional hominid footprints is erroneous" (Renne, et al, 2005, p. 438). Because of the inconsistency of dating methods, scientists don't know which geological period of time to put the footprints into, so they conclude that the tracks are not human footprints. The assumed dates of 40,000 years to 1.3 million years stifle their own evolutionary processes because the footprints would then overturn their esteemed and long-held theories of origins and migration patterns. So in short, they conclude the footprints are not footprints. If the empirical evidence does not fit the theory, they throw out the evidence altogether.

Furthermore, a separate find was discovered by Denver geologist Martin Lockley, of the University of Colorado at Denver, and Arturo Gonzalez, director of the Museo del Desierto at Saltillo, Mexico, who, in late March 2004, found about two dozen footprints left behind by four or five barefoot individuals. The tracks were pressed into now-petrified spring deposits in the Cuatro Cienegas basin of northern Mexico's Coahuila state, south of Texas. The site contains well-preserved tracks with distinct toe impressions. More than three feet of soil once covered the tracks. It is guestimated the tracks are about 10,000 years old based on the fact that some archaeological sites in the Cuatro Cienegas Valley date to that period.

The history of the Cuatro Cienegas tracks began in 1961, when two ancient footprints were uncovered in a quarry. The find didn't create much of a stir at the time and ended up in a dusty museum storage room in Torreon, Mexico.

Gonzalez found them there in the late 1980s and began search-

---

208. Ibid.

ing for their source. A label simply said "Cuatro Cienegas" and listed a suggested age of 10,000 years.

The 200,000-acre Cuatro Cienegas Valley is in the heart of the Chihuahuan Desert. Gonzalez pursued numerous tips but failed to find other fossilized footprints. The footprints were deposited in a limestone-like rock called tufa, which is formed by mineral-rich spring water. Lockley joined Gonzalez and team and in the last hour of the final day of their trip, they found the tufa deposits that produced the initial footprints, along with about two dozen others.

The date of the earliest peopling of the Americas has been controversial ever since the subject had been first broached centuries ago, and is likely to remain so for a long time. In the U.S., the "Clovis first" school of thought held, until very recently, that the Clovis people, dating to not more than 12,000 years or so, were the first Americans. Solid evidence is rapidly accumulating that this is not so and that there are traces of older, perhaps much older, populations all over North, Middle, and South America. Unfortunately, the controversy surrounding the Toloquilla footprints and their date has done nothing to clarify matters.

Dr. Silvia Gonzalez (Gonzalez S., *et al,* 2006) writes in her abstract:

> The timing, route and origin of the first colonialization of the Americas remains one of the most contentious topics in human evolution. A number of migration routes have been suggested and there are different views as to the antiquity of the earliest human occupation. Some believe that settlement happened as early as 30,000 years before present, but most of the currently accepted early sites in North America date to the latest Pleistocene, related to the expansion of the Clovis culture, while the oldest directly radiocarbon-dated human remains are 11,500 years before present. In this context, new evidence is presented in this paper, in the form of human footprints preserved in indurated volcanic ash, to suggest that Central Mexico was inhabited as early as over 40,000 years before present.
>
> Human and animal footprints have been found within the up-

per nedding surfaces the Xalnene volcanic ash layer that outcrops in the Valsequillo Basin, south of Puebla, Mexico. This ash layer was produced by a subaqueous monogenetic volcano erupting within a palaeo–lake, dammed by lava within the Valsequillo Basin during the Pleistocene. The footprints were formed during low stands in lake level along the former shorelines and indicate the presence of humans, deer, canids, big felids, and probably camels and bovids. The footprints were buried by ash and lake sediments as lake levels rose and transgressed across the site. The ash has been dated to at least 40,000 before present by OSL–dating of incorporated, baked lake sediments.

An analysis by Renne P. R. and Feinberg concluded that the identification of these features as hominid footprints is erroneous (Renne, et al, 2005).

In other words, the footprints are not footprints and it is left open what the prints are. If the footprints are not footprints, what are they? Other archaeologists who inspected the footprints *in situ* reported that the impressions were irregular marks that varied in size and depth, and that these marks looked similar to those made by workers excavating sheets of hardened volcanic ash. It was even reported that while the archaeologists were at the site, passing quarry workers claimed to have made the marks in question. These laborers do seem to have a sense of humor or a lot of spare time at work, perhaps both. In any case, marks made by the quarry workers and their equipment have been distinguished by Gonzalez, *et al*, in the original article. Nevertheless, many others are complete with anatomically correct toes and heels clearly visible. There are hundreds of these human fossil footprints on site.

TURKMENISTAN
THE "RUSSIAN PALUXY"

In Turkmenistan there have been reports since the 1980s that human footprints have been found along dinosaur tracks. Sergei Golovin, a Russian geophysicist, details in a 1996 edition of *Creation* magazine that journalist Alexander Bushev "reported in the 31 January 1995 edition of *Komsomolskaya Pravda* (one of the most popular newspapers of the former USSR) that he had journeyed to the plateau near the village of Khodga–Pil in Turkmenistan, and had seen the fossilized prints of dinosaurs and humans together."[209]

Bushev said that the Jurassic plateau (supposedly dated at 200 million years old) is covered by more than 3,000 three–toed footprints made by dinosaurs. The most mysterious fact, Bushev added, "is that among the footprints of dinosaurs, footprints of bare human feet were found!" (op cit).

This was originally published to readers of the English version of *Moscow News* in 1983 (No. 24, p. 10). This is their commentary:

> Who knows, but maybe our very far removed ancestors did mingle with dinosaurs?
>
> "Science might possibly answer that in the affirmative some time in the future," said Professor Kurban Amanniyazov, head of the expedition. "However, at present we don't have enough grounds to say this. We've imprints resembling human footprints, but to date have failed to determine, with any scientific veracity, whom they belong to, after all. If we could prove that they do belong to a humanoid, then it would create a revolution in the science of man."[210]

Turkmenian scientist Kurban Amanniyazov led three expeditions to the dinosaur plateau and found human footprints alongside dinosaur tracks.

Professor Plutalov, a member of the Turkmenian expedition, made a map of the dinosaur tracks on the plateau. The dinosaur plateau is approximately 400 meters long and 300 meters wide. There are over 3,000 well preserved dinosaur tracks on the plateau. In one football field–sized area are 1,253 dinosaur tracks of 65 different species. The plateau has the longest dinosaur trackways in the world, 26 of which are megalosaur trackways. Some of the largest are trackway number 14 at 604 feet, trackway 18 at 741 feet, track-

---

209. Golovin, Sergei, *Creation* 18(4):52, September 1996.
210. Rubtsov, Cr. V., 1983, "Tracking Dinosaurs," *Moscow News,* no. 24, p. 10.

way 22 at 873 feet, and the longest trackway, number 21 at 1,020 feet. The previous record was a trackway in Portugal at 482 feet.[211] The smallest three-toed dinosaur tracks are 7 to 8 inches long while the largest footprint is 28 inches long, a megalosaur footprint that is as large as any discovered in the Jurassic.[212]

Dr. Amanniyazov is simply astonished that there are human or humanlike footprints with the dinosaurs in a layer of Jurassic rock that he estimates to be 200 million years old. He discusses one of the footprints in an article that appeared in a Russian science magazine, *Around the World,* and says: ". . . if we speak about this human footprint, it was made by a human or a humanlike animal. Incredibly, this footprint is on the same plateau where there are dinosaur tracks. We can say the age of the footprint is not 5 or 10, but at least 150 million years old. It is 26cm long, that is Russian size 43 (9.5 American) and we consider that whoever left the footprint was taller than we are."

Dr. Dennis Swift, of the Dinosaur Institute, has investigated and documented this site in recent years. In August of 2000, Swift was officially invited by the Turkmenistan government and the Academy of Science of Turkmenistan to investigate the Koughitang-Tau dinosaur sites. He received permission to conduct many tests and make latex molds of the dinosaur and human footprints. His research is presently ongoing.

OTHER SITES FROM AROUND THE WORLD

EGYPT

Egyptian archaeologists have found what may be the oldest human footprint in history in the country's western desert. Archaeologists

---

211. Near Glen Rose, Texas in the Paluxy River, the author mapped the longest contiguous dinosaur trackway in the Western Hemisphere named the Turnage-Patton Trail. The trackway is 407' & consist of 136 contiguous dinosaur footprints, is interrupted by approximately 56' of river erosion, and then continues. The overall length of the trail is 527'. It was probably made by an adult Acrocanthosaurus dinosaur.

212. Swift, Dennis, 2006-2008, "Dinosaurs and Man" webpage, www.dinosaursandman.com.

found the footprint while exploring a prehistoric site in Siwa, a desert oasis. The footprint was originally imprinted into mud which then hardened to rock. Scientists are using carbon tests on plants found in the rock to determine its age. However, this will not yield any age in which the footprint was made. Khaled Saad, the director of prehistory at the council, said that based on the age of the rock where the footprint was found, it could date back even further than the 3 million–year–old fossil Lucy. It sounds like circular reasoning is at it again.

ASIA

Footprints of a human, the first to be found in Asia, and fossilized animal tracks were discovered on Cheju Island, Korea. Conventional dating techniques have estimated the footprint to that of Paleolithic man dating back to supposedly 50,000 years ago.

More than 100 footprints of ancient man and thousands of horse, elephant, bird, and deer fossil tracks were found in Namcheju–gun on the southern island province of Cheju and along the shores of the island's Andok–myon. The fossils were discovered by Professor Kim Jung–yul of the Korean National University of Education last October. The human footprints that Kim found are 21 to 25 centimeters in length, and the imprints of the foot are clearer than those found in Kenya and Tanzania. Not only are the heel and ball of the foot evident in the imprints but the imprint of the medial arch is also explicit. The Korean Culture Properties Administration is considering naming the area a national monument and has restricted entrance in an effort to preserve the fossils.

TURKEY: THE GEDIZ TRACK

The footprint of a human being, apparently fleeing toward the Gediz River from a volcanic eruption, was discovered in volcanic ash during the construction of a dam. The scientific journal Nature (254:553, [1975]) published a photograph of the footprint which was found in volcanic ash near Demirkopru, Turkey, in 1970. The print is now in the Stockholm Museum of National History. Scientists guestimate its stratigraphic age as being 250,000 years old by the Turkish Mineral

Research and Exploration Institute in Ankara. However, the print was authenticated to be human (H. sapien) by the National Laboratory of Forensic Science in Sweden.

Conclusion

Amazingly, there are no supposed "transitional footprints" that have ever been found in the fossil record. So what if the fossil footprints are from a modern human? The implications are significant. This would imply that: (1) evolution is a fallacy and its theories and timelines are wrong, and (2) greater confidence can be put in the book of Genesis, which states that God created all living things in six days.

Although supposed skeletal remains of humans ancestors have

IF THESE TWO PAIR OF "HOMO SAPIEN SAPIEN" DEFORMED FEET WERE FOUND AS FOSSIL FOOTPRINTS BY EVOLUTIONISTS, THEY WOULD WRONGLY PROCLAIM TO THE WORLD THAT THEY WERE PROOF OF THE MISSING LINK BETWEEN MONKEYS AND MAN!

Sturdy as his staff, José Maria Roa, 87, slogs through the Ecuadorean ooze from which he makes adobe. Forty years at the task have deformed his feet...

THE ABOVE PAIR OF FEET BELONG TO AN INDIVIDUAL WHO LIVES IN A JUNGLE ENVIRONMENT. THE JUNGLE FLOOR IS AN UNEVEN TERRAIN. AS A RESULT OF CONSTANTLY WALKING BAREFOOT ON ROOT COVERED GROUND, HIS FEET HAVE WIDENED IN SUCH A WAY AS TO "DEFORM" TO THAT TERRAIN. THIS IS NOT MACRO-EVOLUTIONARY GENETIC CHANGE!

ANOTHER IMPORTANT FACT TO KEEP IN MIND IS THAT BOTH OF THESE INDIVIDUALS WERE BORN WITH NORMAL HOMO SAPIEN SAPIEN FEET. IMAGOLUTIONISTS CLAIM THAT THESE KINDS OF CHANGES IN THEIR ADULT FEET WILL BE PASSED DOWN TO FUTURE GENERATIONS. EMPIRICAL GENETIC RESEARCH HAS PROVEN THAT EXTERNAL ENVIRONMENTAL CONDITIONS CANNOT ADD INFORMATION TO THE GENETIC CODE OF ANY BIOLOGICAL SYSTEM. IT CAN ONLY STIMULATE ADAPTIVE INFORMATION THAT ALREADY RESIDES IN ANY GIVEN GENETIC CODE.

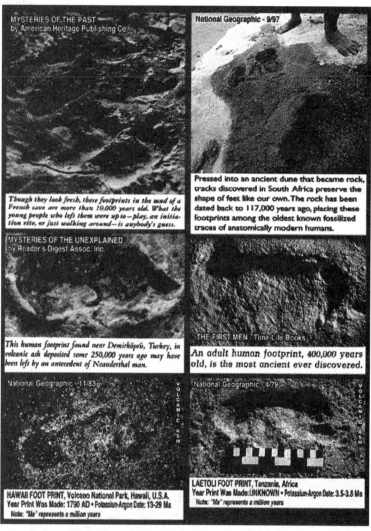

MYSTERIES OF THE PAST
by American Heritage Publishing Co.

National Geographic - 9/97

Though they look fresh, these footprints in the mud of a French cave are more than 10,000 years old. What the young people who left them were up to—play, an initiation rite, or just walking around—is anybody's guess.

Pressed into an ancient dune that became rock, tracks discovered in South Africa preserve the shape of feet like our own. The rock has been dated back to 117,000 years ago, placing these footprints among the oldest known fossilized traces of anatomically modern humans.

MYSTERIES OF THE UNEXPLAINED
by Reader's Digest Assoc. Inc.

This human footprint found near Demirköprü, Turkey, in volcanic ash deposited some 250,000 years ago may have been left by an antecedent of Neanderthal man.

THE FIRST MEN · Time-Life Books

An adult human footprint, 400,000 years old, is the most ancient ever discovered.

National Geographic - 11/83

National Geographic - 4/79

HAWAII FOOT PRINT, Volcano National Park, Hawaii, U.S.A.
Year Print Was Made: 1790 AD • Potassium-Argon Date: 13-29 Ma
Note: "Ma" represents a million years

LAETOLI FOOT PRINT, Tanzania, Africa
Year Print Was Made: UNKNOWN • Potassium-Argon Date: 3.5-3.8 Ma
Note: "Ma" represents a million years

All of these fossil footprints have identified as indistinguishable from modern human footprints. Footprints #2 & 3 are from the Laetoli trackway in Africa. These footprints are said to be *Au. Afarensis,* supposed relatives of "Lucy's family" 3.1 to 3.8 million years ago using the now falsified potassium–argon dating method.

been discovered, they have not revealed any empirical evidence showing the evolution of the human foot. These are human footprints, not ape prints. Apes and men have quite different footprints.

Apes have essentially four hands with an opposable big toe that looks like a thumb. They also have a gait that is different and a tendency to drop on all fours and "knuckle–walk." The ichnological evidence shows humans have been humans all along in the rock strata. Human fossil footprints reveal modern characteristics of human feet and not evolutionary changes over long ages of time. In summary, there simply is no evolutionary change in the human foot. The only conclusion that can be made based on the evidence is that humans have existed on the planet long before the evolutionary timetable indicates.

Leonard Brand and James Florence did some excellent research. They gathered together the great majority of animal fossil footprint records from approximately 800 published papers, as well as from data in five major paleontological museums. This information was then correlated with burial records on the fossils themselves. Comparing it all, they came up with some surprising conclusions:

1. Birds and mammals were buried on about the same levels as the footprints of their species were found. This was in the Quaternary and Tertiary at the very end of the flood.
2. Below these top strata, however, the footprints of amphibians, non–dinosaur reptiles, and dinosaurs were made well below the levels where the bulk of their bodies were buried.

> That second discovery is rather astounding. If long ages had occurred during each strata, then the footprints and bodies should be found together. But if a worldwide single flood was responsible for all the strata, then we would expect to find large numbers of amphibians, reptiles, and dinosaurs walking around earlier in the flood, yet buried later in it. This also holds true for the fossil human footprints found in sedimentary rock.
>
> During the early to middle part of the flood large numbers of amphibians and reptiles were moving about, and thus producing footprints. Later as the flood progressed (upper Jurassic and Cretaceous) there were very few live amphibians or reptiles to produce footprints, except for the large dinosaurs. During the Cre-

taceous when the only footprints preserved were the large dinosaur tracks, there were many amphibian and reptile bodies that
were being buried to produce the abundant Cretaceous body fossils. During the Cenozoic almost no amphibian or reptile footprints
were preserved.

... During the flood the birds and mammals were in the up-
lands, away from the depositional basins, because of ecological
differences and/or more adaptable behavioral responses to the
unusual biological crisis caused by the flood.[213]

The theory of evolution is not indisputable scientific truth as many
people assume. On the contrary, there are glaring contradictions
when the theory of evolution is compared to scientific findings in
such diverse fields as the origin of life, population genetics, comparative anatomy, paleontology, and biochemistry. In a word, evolution
is a theory in "crisis."

That is a description by Prof. Michael Denton, an Australian biochemist and a renowned critic of Darwinism. In his book *Evolution:
A Theory in Crisis* (1985), Denton examined the theory in the light
of different branches of science, and concluded that the theory of
natural selection is very far from providing an explanation for life on
Earth. Denton's intention in offering his criticism was not to show
the correctness of another view, but only to compare Darwinism
with the scientific facts. During the last two decades, many other scientists have published significant works questioning the validity of
Darwin's theory of evolution.

Historians tell us that evolutionary theory that says that vio-
lence and selfishness is the basis of change and improvement has
greatly worsened human morals and produced wars. In reviewing
the desolation which evolutionary theory has produced over the
past 150 years, thoughtful scientists declare that the theory has
greatly hindered the advance of scientific endeavor.

---

213. Brand, Leonard, and James Florence, "Stratigraphic Distribution of
Vertebrate Fossil Footprints Compared with Body Fossils" *Origins*, Vol
9, no. 2 (1982), p. 71.

Lord Solly Zuckerman is one of the most famous and respected scientists in the United Kingdom. For years, he studied the fossil record and conducted many detailed investigations. He was elevated to the peerage for his contributions to science. Zuckerman is an evolutionist. Therefore, his comments on evolution cannot be regarded as ignorant or prejudiced. After years of research on the fossils included in the human evolution scenario, however, he reached the conclusion that there is no truth to the family tree that is put forward.

Zuckerman also advanced an interesting concept of the "spectrum of the sciences," ranging from those he considered scientific to those he considered unscientific. According to Zuckerman's spectrum, the most scientific (dependent on concrete data) fields are chemistry and physics. After them come the biological sciences and then the social sciences. At the far end of the spectrum, which is the part considered to be most unscientific, are extrasensory perception (concepts such as telepathy and the "sixth sense"), and finally human evolution. Zuckerman explains his reasoning as follows: "We then move right off the register of objective truth into those fields of presumed biological science, like extrasensory perception or the interpretation of man's fossil history, where **to the faithful anything is possible—and where the ardent believer is sometimes able to believe several contradictory things at the same time.**"[214]

Robert Locke, the editor of *Discovering Archaeology*, an important publication on the origins of man, writes in that journal, "The Search for Human Ancestors Gives More Heat than Light," quoting the confession of the famous evolutionary paleoanthropologist Tim White: We're all frustrated by "all the questions we haven't been able to answer."[215]

Locke's article reviews the impasse of the theory of evolution on the origins of man and the groundlessness of the misinformation spread about this subject: "Perhaps no area of science is more

---

214. Zuckerman, Solly, *Beyond The Ivory Tower*, Toplinger Publications, New York, 1970, p. 19.
215. Locke, Robert, "Family Fights," *Discovering Archaeology*, July/August 1999, p. 36–39.

contentious than the search for human origins. Elite paleontologists disagree over even the most basic outlines of the human family tree. New branches grow amid great fanfare, only to wither and die in the face of new fossil finds.[216]

The same fact was also recently accepted by Henry Gee, the editor of the well-known journal *Nature*. In his book *In Search of Deep Time*, published in 1999, Gee points out that all the evidence for human evolution "between about 10 and 5 million years ago—several thousand generations of living creatures—can be fitted into a small box." He concludes that conventional theories of the origin and development of human beings are "a completely human invention created after the fact, shaped to accord with human prejudices." He then adds: "To take a line of fossils and claim that they represent a lineage is not a scientific hypothesis that can be tested, but an assertion that carries the same validity as a bedtime story—amusing, perhaps even instructive, but not scientific" (Gee, 1999, p. 126–127).

As we have seen, there is no scientific discovery supporting or propping up the theory of evolution, just some scientists who blindly believe in it. These scientists both believe in the myth of evolution themselves, although it has no scientific foundation, and also make other people believe it by using the media, which cooperates with them. In the pages that follow, we shall examine a few examples of this deceptive misinformation carried out in the name of evolution.

All the scientific deceptions and prejudiced evaluations made to support the theory of evolution show that the theory is a kind of ideology, and not at all a scientific account. Like all ideologies, this one has its fervent supporters who are desperate to prove evolution, no matter the cost. Or they are so dogmatically bound to the theory that every new discovery is perceived as a great proof, even if it has nothing to do with factual information. This is really a very distressing representation for science because it shows that science is being misdirected in the name of evolutionary theory.

In his book *Darwinism: The Refutation of a Myth*, Swedish scientist Søren Løvtrup has this to say: "I suppose that nobody will deny

---

216. Ibid.

that it is a great misfortune if an entire branch of science becomes addicted to a false theory. But this is what has happened in biology: for a long time now people discuss evolutionary problems in a peculiar 'Darwinian' vocabulary—'adaptation,' 'selection pressure,' 'natural selection,' etc.—thereby believing that they contribute to the explanation of natural events. They do not. . . . I believe that one day the Darwinian myth will be ranked the greatest deceit in the history of science."[217]

The pictures on the next page represent some of the falsely dated human fossil footprints. The Hawaii print illustrates why this is true. This footprint is known to have been made in A.D. 1790. The potassium–argon age of the print is dated erroneously at 13–29 million years old! This empirical fact clearly falsifies all potassium–argon dates associated with any fossil, rock, footprints, or otherwise.

In the April 1979 issue of *National Geographic,* preeminent footprint expert Dr. Louise M. Robbins commented on the Laetoli tracks stating, "They looked so human, so modern, to be found in tuffs so old."

There are reasons why evolutionists are so anxious to hold on to a theory that has no evidence to support it, a theory which has been repeatedly disproved. These are important reasons. **Men do not want to be responsible to anyone for their actions.**

"[Man] stands alone in the universe, a unique product of a long, unconscious, impersonal, material process with unique understanding and potentialities. These he owes to no one but himself and it is to himself that he is responsible. He is not the creature of uncontrollable and undeterminable forces, but he is his own master. He can and must decide and make his own destiny."[218]

SEPARATION FROM GOD

The real issue is whether man must think God's thought after him

217. Løvtrup, Søren, *Darwinism: The Refutation of A Myth,* Croom Helm, New York, 1987, p. 422.
218. Simpson, George G., "The World Into Which Darwin Led Us," *Science,* 131 (1980), p. 968.

in order to understand the world correctly or whether man's mind is the ultimate assigner of meaning to brute and orderless facts. . . . Evolutionary thought is popular because it is a world view which facilitates man's attempt to rid himself of all knowledge of the transcendent Creator and promises to secure man's autonomy.[219]

SEXUAL FREEDOM

I had motives for not wanting the world to have meaning; consequently assumed it had none, and was able without any difficulty to find satisfying reasons for this assumption. . . . The philosopher who finds no meaning in the world is not concerned exclusively with a problem in pure metaphysics; he is also concerned to prove there is no valid reason why he personally should not do as he wants to do. . . . For myself, as no doubt for most of my contemporaries, the philosophy of meaninglessness was essentially an instrument of liberation. The liberation we desired was simultaneously liberation from a certain political and economic system and liberation from a certain system of morality. We objected to the morality because it interfered with our sexual freedom.[220][221]

A WAY TO HIDE FROM GOD

Darwinism removed the whole idea of God as the creator of organisms from the sphere of rational discussion. Darwin pointed out that no supernatural designer was needed; since natural selection could account for any new form of life, there is no room for a supernatural agency in its evolution.

—Julian Huxley[222]

---

219. Bahnsen, G. L., "On Worshipping the Creature Rather Than the Creator," *Journal of Christian Reconstruction,* 1 (1974), p. 89.
220. Grandson of evolutionist Thomas Huxley and brother of evolutionist Julian Huxley. Aldous Huxley was one of the most influential writers and philosophers of the twentieth century.
221. Huxley, Aldous, "Confessions of a Professed Atheist," *Report: Perspective on the News,* Vol. 3, June, 1966, p. 19.
222. "At Random, A Television Preview," *Evolution after Darwin* (1960), p. 41.

WE CAN CHOOSE TO LIVE LIKE ANIMALS

In the world of Darwin man has no special status other than his definition as a distinct species of animal. He is in the fullest sense a part of nature and not apart from it. He is akin, not figuratively but literally, to every living thing, be it an amoeba, a tapeworm, a flea, a seaweed, an oak tree, or a monkey—even though the degrees of relationship are different and we may feel less empathy for forty-second cousins like the tapeworms than for, comparatively speaking, brothers like the monkeys.

—George Gaylord Simpson[223]

MEN WOULD RATHER HAVE THE FORBIDDEN TREE THAN THE PRESENCE OF GOD

With this single argument the mystery of the universe is explained, the deity annulled, and a new era of infinite knowledge ushered in.[224]

Scientific evidence points to the Bible as a reliable guide for mankind. Upon opening it, we discover something that no science textbook can provide—the pathway to forgiveness of sin and a new life in Jesus Christ as our Lord and Savior. A national poll which was released in October 2005 was worded in accordance with the publicized concept of design theorists that, although an Intelligence made everything, it occurred millions of years ago.

"[In this Gallup poll] 53 percent of American adults agreed with the statement that God created humans in their present form exactly the way the Bible describes it [in Genesis]. Another 31 percent stood by the Intelligent Design position that humans evolved over millions of years from other forms of life and God guided the process, while 12 percent said humans have evolved from other forms of life and 'God had no part.'"[225]

It is quite clear from this most recent poll that *over half* of Amer-

---

223. Simpson, "The World Into Which Darwin Led Us," p. 970.
224. Haeckel, Ernst, *The Riddle of the Universe* (1899), p. 337.
225. George Gallup Organization, November 10, 2005.

icans in 2005 believe what the Bible teaches about creation, *only a third* believe the position of design theorists, that the Creator made everything millions of years ago (a view which totally disagrees with Genesis), while *only one–eighth* of Americans believe in the obviously ridiculous evolutionary theory, that everything made itself.

Evolutionists are aware that freedom of thought will mean the end of their theory of evolution, and for this reason, they have discouraged thought in academia and public schools. The methods they use are complex and difficult to understand. The evolutionary story is constantly in flux. They use incomprehensible terminology, Latin words, and scientific comparisons, and insist that such things can never be understood by ordinary people. People are thus persuaded and decide from the beginning that they cannot understand and that the fundamentals of evolution can be comprehended only by people of science. The most logical thing then is for people to accept what they say. Between the leaders of academia and the followers, a hierarchy has been established and everyone knows their place.

The suggestion evolution gives to people is, "You are not responsible to anyone because you owe your life to chance." It is a belief system based on death. It is the message given by concepts of Darwinism such as "natural selection" and the "survival of the fittest."

To be an evolutionist it is necessary to believe that living beings were formed from lifeless matter, that reptiles began to fly as a result of a coincidental process, that highly complex organisms such as cells, and eventually eyes and ears, came into existence by random chance. Sea creatures, such as whales, evolved from mammals like bears that went into the sea in search of food. Dinosaurs that ran after flies developed wings and became birds.

It is evident how unreasonable and illogical these presuppositions are. One who reads these words might think that since respected scientists believe these things, they must have proof. There is not the slightest proof—only guesses and suppositions. The decision about these things has already been made; now it is necessary only to believe.

All that is needed to get people to believe in evolution is a single article in a magazine, a book, or a short documentary film. Even if a scientist wishes to, they cannot ask questions which would contradict the Darwinian theory. Those who do so may be ostracized and excluded from academia. In fact, they are "blackballed" in most cases.

Anyone with minimal scientific knowledge knows that there would not be enough time for a fish coming onto the land to grow accustomed to the new environment, and that it would soon die. Anyone who has studied the complex structure of a cell will understand that this miraculous organism could not have come to be through coincidence. However, it is only by investigating and observing that a person will be able to see the truth and overcome their preconceived notions. In order to understand that God created the universe, all one has to do is look at the signature of God in the creation. Psalm 19:1 says, "The heavens declare the glory of God; and the firmament sheweth his handywork." Again in Psalms 97:6: "The heavens declare his righteousness, and all the people see his glory."

The most important aim of the theory is to graft into the human mind the deception that the world was not created by God and that consequently there is no responsibility for adhering to a divine Creator. Evolutionists emphasize this often, pointing out that a human being is his own "master" and responsible only to himself.

The truth is, God created man for His own purpose, to have fellowship with Him. It is our choice to know Him and experience an intimate personal relationship with the Creator of the universe. When one is freed from the evolutionary mindset, the only conclusion one can come to is that there is a supreme Creator of the universe: the God of the Bible.

BIBLIOGRAPHY

Able, E. (1973). *Ancient Views on the Origin of Life.* Farleigh: Dickinson University Press.

Asimov, I. (1970, June). *In the Game of Energy and Thermodynamics You Can't Even Break Even.* Journal of Smithsonian Institute.

Ayala, F. "Nothing in Biology Makes Sense Except in the Light of Evolution: Theodosius Dobzhansky, 1900–1975," *Journal of Heredity,* Vol. 88, No. 3, 1977, p. 3.

Baugh, C. & Wilson, C. 1987. *Dinosaur.* Promise Publishers

----- 1994. *Footprints and the Stones of Time,* Hearthstone Publishing,

Baugh, C. 1999. *Why Do Men Believe Evolution Against All Odds?* Hearthstone Publishing

Behe, M. (1996). *Darwin's Black Box.* New York: Free Press.

Cremo, M. A., & Thompson, R. L. (1993). *Forbidden Archaeology: The Hidden History of the Human Race.* San Diego: Bhaktivedanta Institute.

Dawkins, Richard, *The Blind Watchmaker,* London: W. W. Norton, 1986

Darwin, Charles, *The Origin of Species,* 6th edition, London: John Murray, 1882.

----- *The Origin of Species: A Facsimile of the First Edition,* Cambridge, MA: Harvard University Press, 1964.

Deloison, Y. M. (1997). "The foot bones from Hadar, Ethiopia and the Laetoli, Tanzania footprints. Locomotion of A. *afarensis.*" *American Journal of Physical Anthropology*

Denton, Michael, *Evolution: A Theory in Crisis,* London: Burnett Books, 1985.

Eiseley, Loren, *Darwin's Century,* New York: Doubleday, 1961.

Gee, H. (1999). *In Search of Time: Beyond the Fossil Record to a New History of Life.* New York: The Free Press.

Gillespie, N. C. (1979). *Charles Darwin and the Problem of Creation.* Chicago: University of Chicago Press.

Gonzalez, S., Huddart, D., Bennett, M., and Gonzalez-Huesca, A. (2006). "Human footprints in Central Mexico older than 40,000 years." *Quaternary Science Reviews,* 25, 201–222.

Gore, R. 1997. "The dawn of humans: The first steps." *National Geographic* 191 (2): 72--99.

Grassé, P. (1977). *Evolution of Living Organisms*. New York: Academic Press.

Harper, G. W. (1979, September). *Alternatives to Evolutionism*. School Science Review

Helfinstine, R. 1994. *Texas Tracks and Artifacts*. R. F. Helfinstine (Publisher)

Hoyle, F. and Wickramasinghe, C. (1981). *Evolution from Space*. Colorado: Hollowbrook Publishers.

Hoyle, F. (1983). *The Intelligent Universe: A New View of Creation and Evolution*. London: Michael Joseph Limited.

Huxley, J. (1955). "Evolution and Genetics", Chapter 8 in *What is Science?*, New York: Simon and Schuster

Huxley, J. & Bronowski, J. (1968). *Growth of Ideas*. Englewood Cliffs, NJ: Prentice–Hall.

Johanson, D. & Edey, M. (1981). *Lucy: The Beginnings of Humankind*. New York: Simon and Schuster.

Johnson, P. (1993). *Darwin on Trial*. 2nd Ed., Downers Grove, Illinois: Intervarsity Press.

----- (1997). *Defeating Darwinism by Opening Minds*. Illinois: Intervarsity Press.

Leakey, M. (1979). "Footprints in the ashes of time." *National Geographic*, 155, 446–457.

Leakey, R. 1994. *Origin of humankind*. Basic Books, New York.

Lewin, R. (1980, November 21). "Evolutionary Theory Under Fire." *Science*.

Lipson, H. S. (1988). "A Physicist's View of Darwin's Theory." *Evolution Trends in Plants*

Lubenow, M. 2004. *Bones of Contention*. Grand Rapids, Baker, 1992

Macbeth, N. (1971). *Darwin Retried: An Appeal to Reason*. Boston: Harvard University Press.

Mayr, E. (1978, September). "Evolution." *Scientific American*

Milner, R. *Encyclopedia of Evolution* (1990)

Morgan, E. (1994). *The Scars of Evolution*. New York: Oxford University Press.

Morris, J. (1980). *Tracking Those Incredible Dinosaurs*. Master Books

Morris, H. (1989). *The Long War Against God: the history and impact of the creation/evolution conflict*. Grand Rapids: Baker Book House.

Oldroyd, D. R. (1983). *Darwinian Impacts*. Atlantic Highlands, NJ: Humanities Press.

Raichlen, David, *et al*, (2007). "The Laetoli footprints and early hominin locomotor kinematics," *Journal of Human Evolution*, p. 2

Renne, P., Feinberg, J., and Waters, M. (2005). "Age of Mexican ash with alleged footprints." *Nature*

Robbins, L. M., Wilson, R., and Watson, P. (1981). "Paleontology and Archeology of Jaguar Cave, Tennessee." *Proceedings of the Eight International Congress of Speleology*, 1, 377–380.

Robbins, L. M. (1985). *Footprints: Collection, Analysis, and Interpretations*. Springfield, Illinois: Charles C. Thomas.

Rodman, P.S. & H.M. McHenry (1980). "Bioenergetics of hominid bipedalism." *American Journal of Physical Anthropology*. 52: 103––106.

Sagan, C. (1980). *Cosmos*. New York: Random House.

Spoor, F., Wood, B., & Zonneveld, F. (1994). "Implications of early hominid labyrinthine morphology for evolution of hominid bipedal locomotion." *Nature* 369: 645—648.

Stern, J. & Susman, R. (1983). "The locomotor anatomy of *Australopithecus afarensis*." *American Journal of Physical Anthropology*, 60, 279–318.

Tuttle, R. H. (1981). "Evolution of hominid bipedalism and prehensile capabilities." *Philosophical Transactions of the Royal Society of London*, B 292, 89–94.

----- (1985). "Ape footprints and Laetoli impressions: a response to the SUNY claims." In P. V. Tobias (ed). *Hominid Evolution: Past, Present, and Future*, 129–133.

----- (1987). "Kinesiological inferences and evolutionary implications from Laetoli biped trails G-1, G-2/3, and A." In M. D. Leakey and J. Harris (eds). *Laetoli: A Pliocene Site in Northern Tanzania*, pp. 508–517.

----- March 1990. *Natural History*, pp. 61–64.

Tuttle, R. H., Musiba, D., Webb, M., and Hallgrimsson, B. (1998). "Kinesiological inferences and evolutionary implications from Laetoli biped trails G-1, G-2/3, and A." In M. D. Leakey and J. Harris (eds). *American Journal of Physical Anthropology*.

Webb, S., Cupper, M., and Robins, R. (2006, April). "Pleistocene human footprints from the Willandra Lakes, southeastern Australia." *Journal of Human Evolution*, 50(4), 405–413.

White, T. & Suwa, G. (1987). "Hominid footprints at Laetoli: facts and interpretations." *American Journal of Physical Anthropology*, 72, 485–514.

Wilson, C. (2001). *Crash Goes Darwin*. Pacific Christian Ministries Australia

----- (2007). *The Paluxy River Dinosaur Controversy,* Pacific Christian Ministries Australia

Wood, B. & Richmond, B. G. (2000). "Human evolution: Taxonomy and paleobiology." *Journal of Anatomy.* 196: 19—60

To order any other omniological resource material go to
www.omniology–store.com

To contact the author:
www.myspace.com/omniologyinstitute
email: paluxydragon@yahoo.com

For more information on the human fossil footprints,
check out these websites:

www.omniology.com
www.bible.ca/tracks
www.mtblanco.com
www.creationevidence.org
www.ianjuby.com